Mrs. Kasluf

Scholastic Success With
GRADE 1
WORKBOOK

Scholastic Canada Ltd.

Maps workbook copyright © 2002 by Linda Ward Beech

Cover art by Tom Ungrey and Reggie Holladay
Cover design by Anna Christian
Interior illustrations by Jon Buller, Reggie Holladay, Anne Kennedy,
Kathy Marlin, Bob Masheris, Sherry Neidigh, and Carol Tiernon
Interior design by Quack & Company

ISBN 978-0-545-99023-3
ISBN-10 0-545-99023-8

6 5 4 3 2   Printed in Singapore   08 09 10 11 12 13

Table of Contents

WRITING

"Nothing succeeds like success."

Alexandre Dumas the Elder, 1854

Dear Parent,

Congratulations on choosing this excellent educational resource for your child. Scholastic has long been a leader in educational publishing—creating quality educational materials for use in school and at home for nearly a century.

As a partner in your child's academic success, you'll want to get the most out of the learning experience offered in this book. To help your child learn at home, try following these helpful hints:

❖ Provide a comfortable place to work.

❖ Have frequent work sessions, but keep them short.

❖ Praise your child's successes and encourage his or her efforts. Offer positive help when a child makes a mistake.

❖ Display your child's work and share his or her progress with family and friends.

In this workbook you'll find hundreds of practise pages that keep kids challenged and excited as they strengthen their skills across the classroom curriculum.

The workbook is divided into eight sections: Reading Comprehension; Reading Tests; Traditional Manuscript; Grammar; Writing; Maps; Addition & Subtraction; and Math. You and your child should feel free to move through the pages in any way you wish.

The table of contents lists the activities and the skills practised. And a complete answer key in the back will help you gauge your child's progress.

Take the lead and help your child succeed with the *Scholastic Success With: Grade 1 Workbook!*

The activities in this workbook reinforce age-appropriate skills and will help your child meet the following standards established as goals by leading educators.

Mathematics

★ Uses a variety of strategies when problem-solving

★ Understands and applies number concepts

★ Uses basic and advanced procedures while performing computation

★ Understands and applies concepts of measurement

★ Understands and applies concepts of geometry

Writing

★ Understands and uses the writing process

★ Uses grammatical and mechanical conventions in written compositions

Reading

★ Understands and uses the general skills and strategies of the reading process

★ Can read and understand a variety of literary texts

★ Can understand and interpret a variety of informational texts

Geography

★ Understands the characteristics and uses of maps and globes

★ Knows the location of places, geographic features, and patterns of the environment

Scholastic Success With

READING COMPREHENSION

Tim Can Read

Tim is a good reader. He uses clues to help him read. First, he looks at the picture. That helps him know what the story is about. Next, he reads the title of the story. Now he knows a little more. As he reads the story, the words make pictures in his mind.

Colour in the book beside the correct answer.

1. Who is Tim?

 a good reader   a math whiz

2. What does Tim do first?

 reads the story   looks at the picture

3. What else helps Tim know what the story will be about?

 the title   the page number

4. As he reads, what makes pictures in Tim's mind?

 the letters   the words

 Now you can try reading the stories in this book the way that Tim does. If you do, you will be a good reader, too! Write the name of your favourite book here.

Trucks

 *The **main idea** tells what the whole story is about.*

Trucks do important work. Dump trucks carry away sand and rocks. Cement trucks have a barrel that turns round and round. They deliver cement to workers who are making sidewalks. Fire trucks carry water hoses and firefighters. Gasoline is delivered in large tank trucks. Flatbed trucks carry wood to the people who are building houses.

Find the sentence in the story that tells the main idea. Write it in the circle below. Then draw a line from the main idea to all the trucks that were described in the story.

Write the sentence that tells the main idea on another sheet of paper. Draw a picture that tells about the sentence.

Circus Clowns

*The **main idea** tells what the whole story is about.*

Today I went to the circus. My favourite part of the circus was the clowns. Clowns can do funny tricks. A clown named Pinky turned flips on the back of a horse. Fancy Pants juggled balls while he was singing a funny song. Happy Hal made balloons into animal shapes. Then twelve clowns squeezed into a tiny car and rode away.

Colour in the ball that tells the main idea.

Pinky rides a horse.

Balloons can be shaped like animals.

Clowns can do funny tricks.

Clowns drive tiny cars.

Fancy Pants sang a song.

Your Name

When you were born, your parents thought of a name for you. You might be named after someone in the family. Maybe you were named after a movie star! Almost every name has a meaning. Pamela means *honey*. Henry means *master of the house*. Ellen means *bright*. Sometimes books about baby names tell the meanings. Many of the meanings will surprise you!

Circle the name below that has the main idea of the story in it.

SAM (I want to be a movie star!) *KATE* (Names have special meanings.)

To find out the meanings of the names in the puzzle below, follow each string of beads. Copy the letters on each bead in order in the boxes.

Casey means ⬚⬚⬚⬚⬚ .   George means ⬚⬚⬚⬚⬚⬚ .

Sarah means ⬚⬚⬚⬚⬚⬚⬚

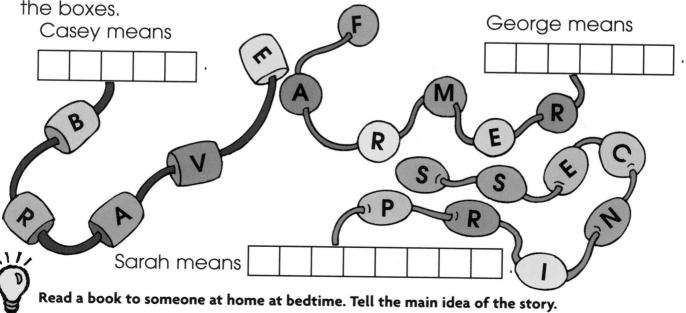

💡 **Read a book to someone at home at bedtime. Tell the main idea of the story.**

Striped Critters

Details *are parts of a story. Details help you understand what the story is about.*

Skunks are small animals that live in the woods. They have black fur with one or two white stripes down their backs. Bugs are their favourite food. They also eat mice. If a skunk raises its tail, run away! Skunks can spray a very smelly liquid at anyone who bothers them.

Write the answers in the crossword puzzle.

Across:

2. What colour are the stripes on a skunk's fur?

5. What is a skunk's favourite food?

Down:

1. What is another thing that skunks like to eat?

2. Where do skunks live?

3. What does a skunk raise when it is getting ready to spray?

4. What should you do if a skunk raises its tail?

Use details to describe your favourite animal.

Ricky's Wish

 Details *are parts of a story. Details help you understand what the story is about.*

Ricky loved to go camping. One day during reading class, he began to daydream about camping in the mountains. He thought about going fishing and riding horses. It would be fun to gather logs to build a campfire and cook hot dogs. He and his dad could set up the tent near some big trees. He wished he were in his canoe right now. Just then, Ricky heard his teacher say, "Ricky, it is your turn to read." Oh no! He had lost the place!

Circle these things from the story hidden in the picture below: a fish, a fishing pole, a log for the campfire, a hot dog, a tree, and a canoe.

1. Where was Ricky during this story? _____

   _____

2. Where would Ricky like to have been? _____

   _____

 What do you like to daydream about? Write about it using details.

Going to Grammy's

Kelly is going to spend the night with her grandmother. She will need to take her pajamas, a shirt, and some shorts. Into the suitcase go her toothbrush, toothpaste, and hairbrush. Grammy told her to bring a swimsuit in case it was warm enough to swim. Mom said to pack her favourite pillow and storybooks. Dad said, "Don't forget to take Grammy's sunglasses that she left here last week." Now Kelly is ready to go!

1. Colour the things that Kelly packed in her suitcase.

2. A compound word is a big word that is made up of two little words. For example, cow + boy = cowboy. Find 8 compound words in this story and circle them.

On the back of this page, make a list of things you would pack if you were going to spend the night at your grandmother's house.

Mr. Lee's Store

 *Story events that can really happen are **real**. Story events that are make-believe are **fantasy**.*

At night, Mr. Lee locked the store and went home. That's when the fun began! The ketchup bottles stood in rows like bowling pins. Then the watermelon rolled down the aisle and knocked them down. The chicken wings flew around the room. Cans of soup stacked themselves higher and higher until they laughed so hard that they tumbled over. Carrots danced with bananas. Then it was morning. "Get back in your places!" called the milk jug. "Mr. Lee is coming!" Mr. Lee opened the door and went right to work.

Circle the cans that are make-believe.

ketchup bottles and a watermelon bowling	a talking milk jug	dancing bananas
chicken wings that can fly all by themselves	Mr. Lee went to work.	laughing soup cans
Mr. Lee went home at night.	dancing carrots	a grocery store

 Draw a picture of the story on another piece of paper.

Cool Clouds

Have you ever looked up in the sky and seen a cloud that is shaped like an animal or a person? Big, white, puffy clouds float along like soft marshmallows. In cartoons, people can sit on clouds and bounce on them. But clouds are really just tiny drops of water floating in the air. You can understand what being in a cloud is like when it is foggy. Fog is a cloud on the ground!

Read each sentence below. If the sentence could really happen, colour the cloud blue. If the sentence is make-believe, colour it orange.

Clouds float in the sky.

A cartoon dog sleeps on a cloud.

Clouds are made of tiny drops of water.

Animal shapes in clouds are made by the Cloud Fairy.

Clouds are big blobs of whipped cream.

Clouds are made of marshmallows.

Fog is a cloud on the ground.

Birds can hop around on clouds.

Draw a picture to show a real cloud. Then draw a make-believe cloud.

Fun at the Farm

 Story events that can really happen are **real**. *Story events that are make-believe are* **fantasy**.

Read each sentence below. If it could be real, circle the picture. If it is make-believe, put an X on the picture.

 Dairy cows give milk.

 The farmer planted pizza and hamburgers.

 The pig said,"Let's go to the dance tonight!"

 The mouse ate the dinner table.

 The hay was stacked in the barn.

 The chickens laid golden eggs.

 The green tractor ran out of gas.

 The newborn calf walked with wobbly legs.

 The goat and the sheep got married by the big tree.

 Two crickets sang "Mary Had a Little Lamb."

 Horses sat on the couch and watched TV.

 Rain made the roads muddy.

 Four little ducks swam in the pond.

 The farmer's wife baked a pumpkin pie.

 On another sheet of paper, write one make-believe sentence about the farmer's house and one real sentence about it.

Ready for School

 Sequencing *means putting the events in a story in the order they happened.*

Tara could hardly wait for school to start. Mom drove her to the store to buy school supplies. They bought pencils, crayons, scissors, and glue. When Tara got home, she wrote her name on all of her supplies. She put them in a paper sack. The next day, Tara went to school, but the principal told her and the other children to go back home. A water leak had flooded the building. Oh no! Tara would have to wait another whole week!

Number the pictures in the order that they happened in the story.

Colour the supplies that Tara bought.

Swimming Lessons

 Sequencing *means putting the events in a story in the order they happened.*

Last summer I learned how to swim. First, the teacher told me to hold my breath. Then I learned to put my head under water. I practiced kicking my feet. While I held on to a float, I paddled around the pool. Next, I floated to my teacher with my arms straight out. Finally, I swam using both my arms and my legs. I did it! Swimming is fun! This summer, I want to learn to dive off the diving board.

Number the pictures in the order that they happened in the story.

Unscramble the letters to tell what the person in the story wants to do next.

EALNR   **OT**   **IVDE**

___ ___ ___ ___ ___   ___ ___   ___ ___ ___ ___

 What would you like to learn to do? Draw four pictures on the back of your paper to show how to do it.

Shapes in the Sky

➡ *Be sure to read directions carefully.*

Follow the directions.

1. Outline each star with a blue crayon. Then colour each one red.

2. Colour one moon yellow. Colour the other one orange.

3. Draw a face on every sun.

4. Write the number of stars inside the star.

5. Write the number of moons inside the moon.

6. Write the number of suns inside the sun

7. Add the three numbers you wrote together to find the total number of shapes.

   _____ + _____ + _____ = _____

8. Which two shapes belong in the night sky?

   _____ and _____

 Draw a picture of the sun with nine planets around it. Write EARTH on our planet.

My Monster

 Be sure to read directions carefully. Look for key words like circle, underline, *and* colour.

I saw a scary monster who lived in a cave. He had shaggy fur and a long, striped tail. He had ugly, black teeth. His three horns were shaped like arrows. His nose was crooked. One of his feet was bigger than the other three. "Wake up! Time for breakfast," Mom said. Oh, good! It was only a dream.

Follow the directions.

1. **What did the monster's tail look like? Circle it.**

2. **What did the monster's teeth look like? Draw a box around them.**

3. **What did the monster's horns look like? Colour them green.**

4. **What did the monster's nose look like? Underline it.**

5. **What did the monster's feet look like? Colour them red.**

6. **Which one of these is the correct picture of the monster? Draw a cave around him.**

Fun at the Beach

Jack and Joni went to the beach today. Mom spread a blanket on the sand, and they had a picnic. It got very hot, so Jack and Joni jumped into the cold water. They climbed onto a big yellow raft. The waves made the raft go up and down. Later, they played in the sand and built sandcastles. Jack and Joni picked up pretty shells. Joni found a starfish. What a fun day!

1. Colour the pictures below that are from the story. Put an X on the ones that don't belong.

2. In the third sentence, find two words that are opposites of each other and circle them with a red crayon.

3. In the fifth sentence, find two more words that are opposites of each other and circle them with a blue crayon.

4. Draw a box around the compound word that tells what Joni found.

5. What colour was the raft? Show your answer by colouring the picture at the top of the page.

Write three sentences that tell how to get ready to play your favorite sport.

My New Rug

 *When you use your own thoughts to answer the question, "How could that have happened?", you are **drawing conclusions**.*

I got a fancy rug today. It was made of brightly-coloured yarn. I placed it on the floor in front of the TV and sat on it. All of a sudden, it lifted me up in the air! The rug and I flew around the house. Then out the door we went. High above the trees, we soared like an eagle. Finally, it took me home, and we landed in my backyard.

How could that have happened? To find out, use your crayons to trace over each line. Use a different colour on each line. Write the letter from that line in the box at the bottom of the rug.

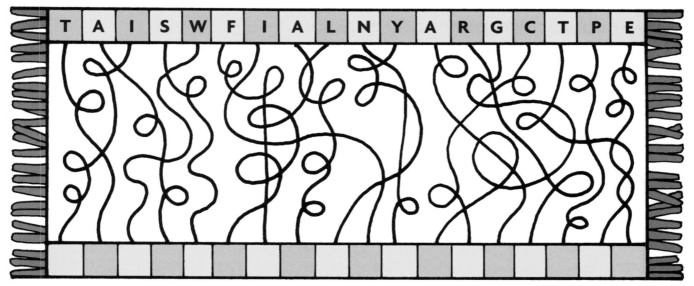

T	A	I	S	W	F	I	A	L	N	Y	A	R	G	C	T	P	E

Could this story really happen? Draw a rug around your answer.

Yes   **No**

 You left your ball on the steps. Your mother came down the steps carrying the laundry basket. Draw a picture of what you think happened.

Polly Want a Cracker?

Have you ever heard a parrot talk? Parrots are able to copy sounds that they hear. You can train a parrot to repeat words, songs, and whistles. But a parrot cannot say words that it has never heard. People can use words to make new sentences, but a parrot cannot.

Read each sentence. If it is true, colour the parrot under True. If it is false, colour the parrot under False.

True   False

1. You could teach a parrot to sing "Happy Birthday."

2. You could ask a parrot any question, and it could give the answer.

3. A parrot could make up a fairy tale.

4. If a parrot heard your mom say, "Brush your teeth," every night, he could learn to say it, too.

5. It is possible for a parrot to repeat words in French.

 Write what would happen if a parrot heard you say, "No, I can't" too often.

You Be the Artist

 Picturing a story can help the reader understand it better.

An artist drew the pictures that are in this book. Now it is your turn to be the artist! Read each sentence very carefully. Draw exactly what you read about in the sentence.

1. The green and yellow striped snake wiggled past the ants.

```
┌─────────────────────────────────────┐
│                                     │
│                                     │
│                                     │
│                                     │
│                                     │
└─────────────────────────────────────┘
```

2. Wildflowers grew along the banks of the winding river.

```
┌─────────────────────────────────────┐
│                                     │
│                                     │
│                                     │
│                                     │
│                                     │
└─────────────────────────────────────┘
```

3. On her sixth birthday, Shannon had a pink birthday cake shaped like a butterfly.

```
┌─────────────────────────────────────┐
│                                     │
│                                     │
│                                     │
│                                     │
│                                     │
└─────────────────────────────────────┘
```

 Now write your own sentence and illustrate it.

A Stormy Day

Big, black clouds appeared in the sky. Lightning struck the tallest tree. The scared cow cried, "Moo!" It rained hard. Soon there was a mud puddle by the barn door. Hay blew out of the barn window.

Read the story above. Then go back and read each sentence again. Add to the picture everything that the sentences describe.

Who Am I?

 Use details from the story to make decisions about the characters.

Circle the picture that answers the riddle.

1. I have feathers. I also have wings, but I don't fly. I love to swim in icy water. Who am I?

2. I am 3 weeks old. I drink milk. I cry when my diaper is wet. Who am I?

3. I live in the ocean. I swim around slowly, looking for something to eat. I have six more arms than you have. Who am I?

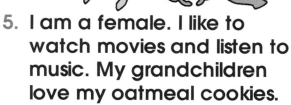

4. I am an insect. If you touch me, I might bite you! I make tunnels under the ground. I love to come to your picnic! Who am I?

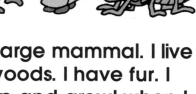

5. I am a female. I like to watch movies and listen to music. My grandchildren love my oatmeal cookies. Who am I?

6. I am a large mammal. I live in the woods. I have fur. I stand up and growl when I am angry. Who am I?

7. I wear a uniform. My job is to help people. I ride on a big red truck. Who am I?

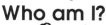 Write your own riddle and let the class guess the answer.

What's Going On?

 Use story details to help you make decisions about the story.

James was the first boy in Miss Lane's class to find red spots on his face and arms. He scratched until his mom came to take him home. A week later, Amy and Jana got the spots. The next Monday, six more children were absent. Finally, everyone got well and came back to school. But, this time Miss Lane was absent. Guess what was wrong with her!

Colour red spots on the correct answers.

1. What do you think was wrong with the children?

sore throats   chicken pox   broken arms

2. How do you know the spots were itchy?

James scratched them.

Amy said, "These spots itch!"

3. How many children in all got sick?

2   5   9   4

4. Why do you think Miss Lane was absent? Write your answer.

 Draw a picture of what Miss Lane might look like with chicken pox!

Make a Cartoon

Read the sentence below each picture. In the bubbles, write what each character could be saying.

Mr. Giraffe asked Mr. Zebra why he had stripes. Mr. Zebra didn't know.

Mr. Giraffe said that he should ask Mrs. Owl. Mr. Zebra agreed.

Mr. Zebra asked Mrs. Owl why he had stripes. Mrs. Owl laughed.

Mrs. Owl told Mr. Zebra that the Magic Fairy painted him that way!

If Mr. Giraffe asked Mrs. Owl why he had such a long neck, what do you think she would say?

Clean Your Room

 Grouping like things together makes it easier to remember what you read.

Mom says, "Let's go out for ice cream! Clean your room, and then we will go." Your room is a mess. You need to put the blocks in the basket. The crayons must go in their box. The books must go on the shelf, and the marbles go in the jar. You can do it. Just think about that hot fudge sundae!

Draw a line from each item on the floor to the place it belongs. Colour what you could use in school red. Colour what are toys blue.

Circle the food that does not belong in an ice cream store.

 Fold a sheet of paper in half. Write "hot" on one side and "cold" on the other side. Draw four foods on each side of the paper that go with the heading.

Going to the Mall

 Look for similarities when grouping items.

Read the words in the Word Box. Write each word in the place where you would find these things at the mall.

Word Box

tickets	sandals	high heels	beans	big screen
tulip bulbs	peppers	fertilizer	popcorn	gardening gloves
sneakers	burritos	boots	pots	candy	tacos

Sandie's Shoe Store

_____
_____
_____
_____

Movie Town Cinema

_____
_____
_____
_____

PEPE'S MEXICAN FOOD

_____
_____
_____
_____

Gale's Gardening Goodies

_____
_____
_____
_____

 On another sheet of paper, draw the following items in a toy store or a clothing store: jump rope, blue jeans, basketball, doll, sweatshirt, stocking cap, wooden train, pajamas.

My Favourites

This page is all about you! Read the categories and write your own answers.

My Favourite TV Shows	My Favourite Foods	My Favourite Sports
_____	_____	_____
_____	_____	_____
_____	_____	_____

Draw two of your favourite people here and write their names.

Favourite Color

_____

Favourite Holiday

_____

Favourite Song

_____

Favourite Movie

_____

Favourite School Subject

_____

Favourite Thing to Do After School

_____

Favourite Thing to Do With My Family

_____

Trade pages with friends and read what they wrote. You might get to know them a little better!

Ouch!

 Use story details to make a guess of what will happen next.

Mia and Rosa were playing hospital. Mia was the patient, and Rosa was the doctor. Rosa pretended to take Mia's temperature. "You have a fever," she said. "You will have to lie down." Mia climbed onto the top bunk bed. "You need to sleep," Dr. Rosa said. Mia rolled over too far and fell off the top bunk. "O-o-o-h, my arm!" yelled Mia. Her mother came to look. It was broken!

What do you think happened next? Write your answer here.

_____

To find out if your answer is correct, finish the sentence below by colouring only the spaces that have a dot in them.

Mia had to go to

 If Mia hadn't fallen off the bed, how do you think this story would have ended? Draw your answer.

What Will Sam Do?

One day, Sam was riding his bike to the baseball game. He had to be on time. He was the pitcher. Just ahead, Sam saw a little boy who had fallen off his bike. His knee was bleeding, and he was crying. Sam asked him if he was okay, but the boy couldn't speak English. Sam knew the boy needed help getting home. If he stopped to help, he might be late for the game. Sam thought about it. He knew he had to do the right thing.

What do you think Sam did next? There are two paths through the maze. Draw a line down the path that shows what you think Sam did next.

What sentence from the story gives you a hint about what Sam decided to do? Write that sentence below.

 The maze shows two ways the story could end. Draw a different ending to the story and tell about your picture.

Riddle Fun

 Compare *means to look for things that are the same.*
Contrast *means to look for things that are different.*

To solve the riddles in each box, read the clues in the horse.
Then write the letters in the blanks with the matching numbers.

What kind of food does a racehorse like to eat?

___ ___ ___ ___   ___ ___ ___ ___
11   5   10   3   11   9   9   2

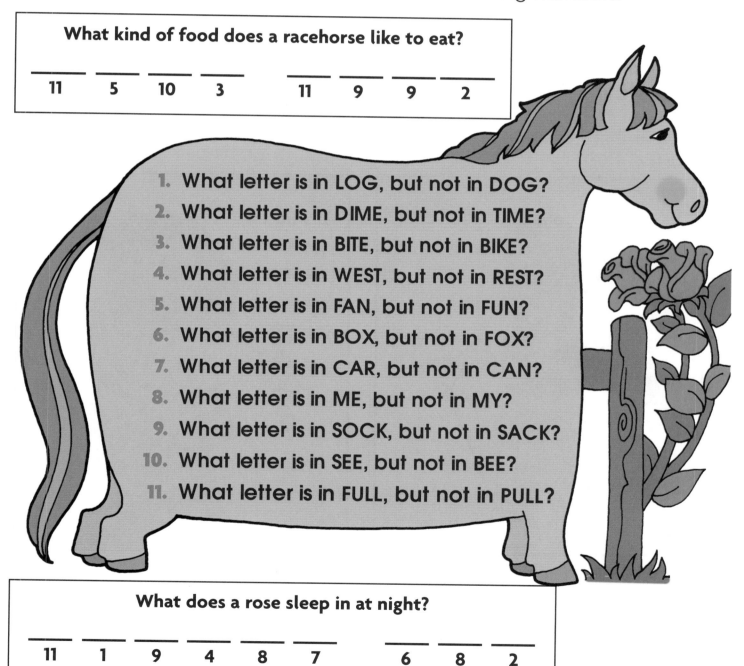

1. What letter is in LOG, but not in DOG?
2. What letter is in DIME, but not in TIME?
3. What letter is in BITE, but not in BIKE?
4. What letter is in WEST, but not in REST?
5. What letter is in FAN, but not in FUN?
6. What letter is in BOX, but not in FOX?
7. What letter is in CAR, but not in CAN?
8. What letter is in ME, but not in MY?
9. What letter is in SOCK, but not in SACK?
10. What letter is in SEE, but not in BEE?
11. What letter is in FULL, but not in PULL?

What does a rose sleep in at night?

___ ___ ___ ___ ___ ___   ___ ___ ___
11   1   9   4   8   7   6   8   2

Twins

Holly and Polly are twins. They are in Grade 1. They look just alike, but they are very different. Holly likes to play softball and soccer. She likes to wear her hair braided when she goes out to play. She wears sporty clothes. Recess is her favourite part of school. Polly likes to read books and paint pictures. Every day she wears a ribbon in her hair to match her dress. Her favourite thing about school is going to the library. She wants to be a teacher some day.

Look at the pictures of Holly and Polly. Their faces look alike. Circle the things in both pictures that are different from each other.

Draw two lines under the words that tell what Holly and Polly do that is the same.

They play sports.   They love to paint.   They are in Grade 1.

Write rhyming names for twins that are boys. What is alike about them? What is different?

Soldier Dads

Juan's dad and Ann's dad are soldiers. Juan's dad is a captain in the Navy. He sails on the ocean in a large ship. Ann's dad is a pilot in the Air Force. He flies a jet. Juan and Ann miss their dads when they are gone for a long time. They write them letters and send them pictures. It is a happy day when their dads come home!

Draw a ☺ in the column under the correct dad.
Some sentences may describe both dads.

	Juan's dad	Ann's dad	Both dads
1. He is a captain.			
2. He works on a ship.			
3. Sometimes he is gone for a long time.			
4. He is a pilot.			
5. His child writes to him.			
6. He is in the Air Force.			
7. He is in the Navy.			
8. It is a happy time when he comes home.			
9. He flies a jet.			
10. He is a soldier.			

Dinosaur Clues

How do we know that dinosaurs were real? It is because their bones have been found in rocks. Sometimes scientists have found dinosaur footprints where mud later turned to stone. These kinds of rocks are called fossils. Fossils give us clues about how big the dinosaurs were. Some were small and some were very large. Scientists say a diplodocus was as big as three school buses!

1. Colour the picture that shows scientists working.

2. Colour the picture of a fossil.

3. Colour the picture of a diplodocus.

 Find and write the names of three more dinosaurs.

Name _____

Amazing Animal Facts

Read each sentence. Then colour the picture that tells the meaning of the underlined word.

1. Sea lions sleep in the water with one <u>flipper</u> up in the air.

2. Even though whale sharks are the biggest fish in the world, they are <u>harmless</u> to people.

3. Horses use their tails to <u>swat</u> pesky flies.

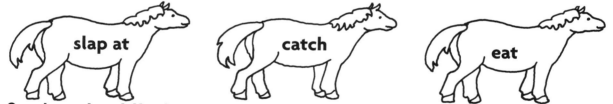

4. Snakes <u>shed</u> their old skins and grow new ones.

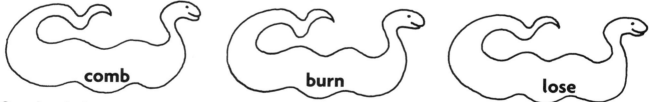

5. Squirrels <u>bury</u> acorns and nuts to eat when winter comes.

 Write an interesting fact about two other animals.

A Tiny Town

Have you ever seen a prairie dog <u>town</u>? That's where <u>prairie dogs</u> live, but there are no buildings or houses. They live underground. They dig deep into the dirt making <u>burrows</u>. Along the burrows, here and there, are <u>chambers</u> for sleeping or storing food. One chamber is lined with grass for the babies. Sometimes prairie dogs have <u>pests</u> in their town, like rattlesnakes!

Use the code below to learn what some of the words in the story mean. Copy the matching letters in the blanks.

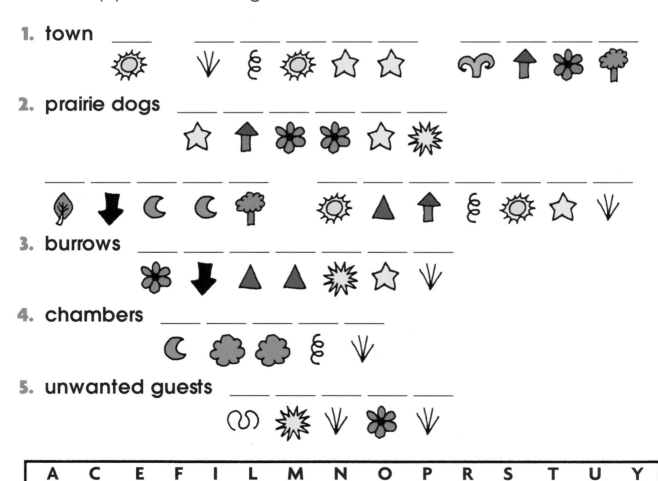

Oops!

*In a story, there is usually a reason something happens.
This is the **cause**. What happens as a result is the **effect**.*

Sandy went on a vacation in the
mountains with her parents and little
brother Austin. They were staying in a
small cabin without any electricity or
running water. It was fun to have
lanterns at night and to bathe in the
cold mountain stream. The biggest
problem for Sandy was she missed her best friend, Kendra. Sandy
found her dad's cell phone and called Kendra. They talked for
nearly an hour! When Sandy's dad went to call his office, the cell
phone was dead. He was NOT a happy camper!

Draw a line to match the first part of each sentence to the second
part that makes it true.

1. **Sandy used lanterns
   at night because**

2. **Sandy and Austin
   bathed in a stream
   because**

3. **Sandy felt better
   about missing
   Kendra because**

4. **Sandy's dad could
   not call his office
   because**

Write about something you did that caused a
huge "effect."

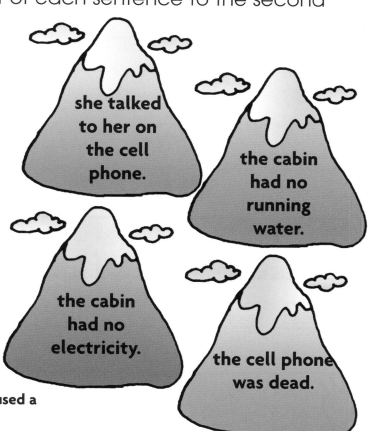

she talked
to her on
the cell
phone.

the cabin
had no
running
water.

the cabin
had no
electricity.

the cell phone
was dead.

Wanda Wiggleworm

 *In a story, there is usually a reason something happens. This is the **cause**. What happens as a result is the **effect**.*

Wanda Wiggleworm was tired of living alone in the flowerpot, so she decided to live it up. Last night, Wanda went to the Ugly Bug Ball. She looked her best, all slick and slimy. Carl Caterpillar asked her to dance. They twisted and wiggled around and around to the music. All of a sudden, they got tangled up. They tried to get free, but instead, they tied themselves in a knot! What would they do? They decided to get married, and they lived happily ever after.

Unscramble each sentence about the story.
Write the new sentence on the line.

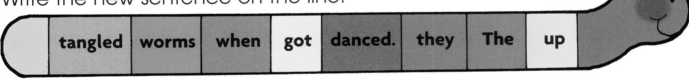

| tangled | worms | when | got | danced. | they | The | up |

_____

_____

| in | knot | They | married. | a | they | were | so | got | tied |

_____

_____

💡 **Tim fell asleep on his raft while playing in the lake. Draw a picture of what you think the effect was on Tim.**

School Rules

It is important to follow the rules at school. Read each rule below. Find the picture that shows what would happen if students DID NOT follow that rule. Write the letter of the picture in the correct box.

1. You must walk, not run, in the halls. ▢

2. Do not chew gum at school. ▢

3. Come to school on time. ▢

4. When the fire alarm rings, follow the leader outside. ▢

5. Listen when the teacher is talking. ▢

6. Keep your desk clean. ▢

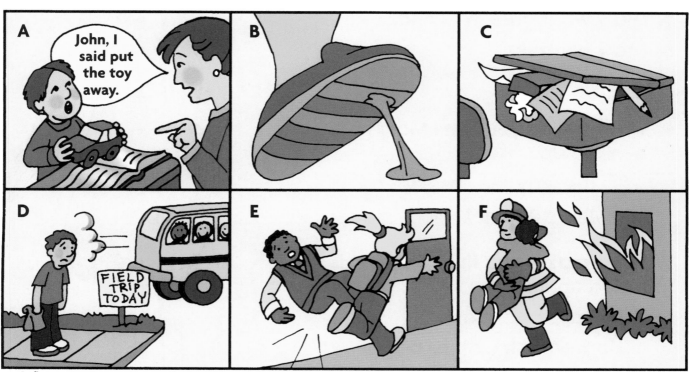

 Write a school rule that you must obey. Draw a picture of what might happen if you do not.

Mixed-Up Margie

 A character is a person or animal in a story. To help readers understand a character better, a story often gives details about the character.

Once upon a time there was a mixed-up queen named Margie. She got things mixed up. She wore her crown on her arm. She wore a shoe on her head. She painted every fingernail a different colour. Then she painted her nose red! She used a fork to hold her hair in place. She wore a purple belt around her knees. The king didn't mind. He always wore his clothes backward!

Use the story and your crayons to help you follow these instructions:

1. Draw Margie's crown.
2. Draw her shoe.
3. Paint her fingernails and nose.
4. Draw what goes in her hair.
5. Draw her belt.

Circle the correct answer:

6. **What makes you think Margie is mixed up?**

   the way she dresses

   the way she talks

7. **What makes you think the king is mixed up, too?**

   He talks backward.

   He wears his clothes backward.

 Pretend tomorrow is Mixed-Up Day. Describe what you will wear as a mixed-up character.

Miss Ticklefoot

I love Miss Ticklefoot. She is my Grade 1 teacher.

To find out more about her, read each sentence below. Write a word in each blank that tells how she feels. The Word Box will help you.

Word Box

| sad | scared | silly | worried | happy | surprised |

1. **Miss Ticklefoot smiles when we know the answers.**

   _____

2. **She is concerned when one of us is sick.**

   _____

3. **She makes funny faces at us during recess.**

   _____

4. **She cried when our fish died.**

   _____

5. **She jumps when the fire alarm rings.**

   _____

6. **Her mouth dropped open when we gave her a present!**

   _____

Different Friends

When Ty was four years old, he had two make-believe friends named Mr. Go-Go and Mr. Sasso. They lived in Ty's closet. When there was no one else around, Ty talked to Mr. Go-Go while he played with his toys. Mr. Go-Go was a good friend. He helped put Ty's toys away. Mr. Sasso was not a good friend. Some days he forgot to make Ty's bed or brush Ty's teeth. One day he even talked back to Ty's mother. Another day Dad said, "Oh my! Who wrote on the wall?" Ty knew who did it . . . Mr. Sasso!

Read the phrase inside each crayon. If it describes Mr. Go-Go, colour it green. If it describes Mr. Sasso, colour it red. If it describes both, colour it yellow.

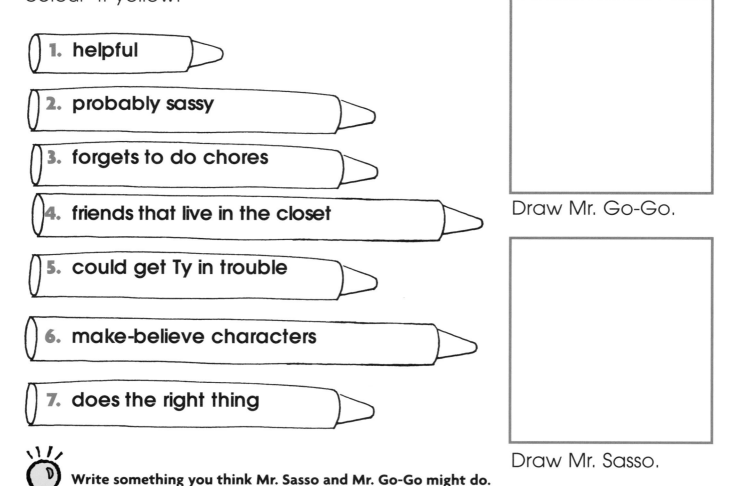

1. helpful

2. probably sassy

3. forgets to do chores

4. friends that live in the closet

5. could get Ty in trouble

6. make-believe characters

7. does the right thing

Draw Mr. Go-Go.

Draw Mr. Sasso.

Write something you think Mr. Sasso and Mr. Go-Go might do.

Poetry

A poem paints a picture with words. It often uses rhyming words.

Colourful Sky
When thunderstorms are near
Coloured strips appear.
At the end, I'm told
There'll be a pot of gold.

Draw what it is.

1. **Draw a red line under the word that rhymes with <u>near</u>.**
2. **Draw a green line under the word that rhymes with <u>told</u>.**

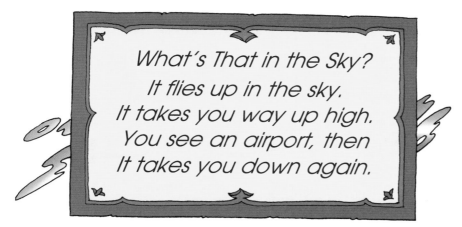

What's That in the Sky?
It flies up in the sky.
It takes you way up high.
You see an airport, then
It takes you down again.

Draw what it is.

3. **Draw a blue circle around the word that rhymes with <u>sky</u>.**
4. **Draw a brown circle around the word that rhymes with <u>then</u>.**
5. **Finish this two-line poem:**

I wish that I could see

A giant bumble_____.

Draw what it is.

Now see if you can make up your own two-line poem using these rhyming words at the end of each line: GO and SNOW.

A Fable

 A fable is a story that teaches a lesson. This fable was written many, many years ago.

The Dog and His Shadow

A dog carried a piece of meat in his mouth. He crossed over a river on a low bridge. He looked down into the water and saw his reflection. It looked like another dog with a piece of meat larger than his. The dog snapped at the other dog's meat. When he did, his own meat dropped into the water. Now the dog didn't have any meat at all.

Draw a box around the lesson that the story teaches:

1. **Two dogs are better than one.**

2. **Don't be greedy. Be happy with what you have.**

Colour only the pictures of things that you read about in the story:

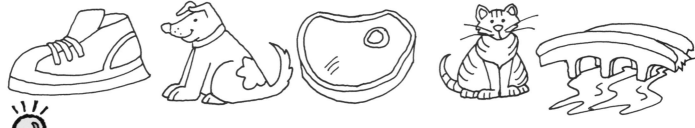

Write a complete sentence telling what the dog should have done.

Library Books

 A library has many different kinds of books.

It is fun to check books out of the library. Have you ever read *Rainbow Fish* by Marcus Pfister? It is a story about a very special fish. His scales were blue, green, and purple. He also had some shiny, silver scales. The other fish wanted him to share his shiny scales with them, but he said no. No one would be his friend. Later, he decided to give each fish one of his shiny scales. It was better to lose some of his beauty and have friends than to keep them to himself.

Connect the dots. You will see something from the book.

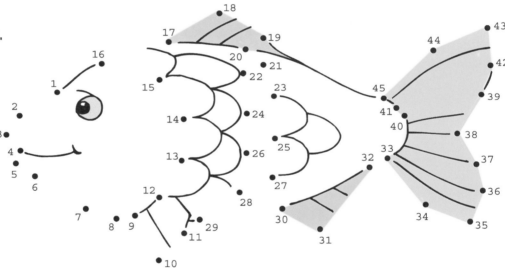

1. Draw a blue circle around the word that tells what this book is about:

    running　　　　lying　　　　sharing　　　　eating

2. Copy the name of the author here.

   _____

   _____

 If you grew up to be an author, what would you write about? Make a pretty book cover that includes the title of your book.

Scholastic Success With

TESTS: READING

Reading Skills Practise Test 1

A. Phonic Analysis: Consonants and Vowels
Look at each picture.
Write the missing letter on the blank line.

Sample	1.	2.
_____ **un**	b _____ **d**	_____ **at**
3.	**4.**	**5.**
_____ **og**	_____ **ug**	s _____ **ck**

B. Vocabulary: Picture-Word Match
Circle the word that names each picture.

Sample	1.	2.	3.
cat	dig	run	car
can	pet	bun	rock
cot	pig	rat	lick

C. High-frequency Word Match

Circle the word your teacher says out loud.

Sample	1.	2.	3.
the	are	will	his
of	my	who	sad
and	like	he	has

D. Grammar, Usage, and Mechanics

Each sentence has a mistake.
Write each sentence correctly on the blank line.

Sample My bike is red

_____

1. i like to run.

_____

2. Did you see it

_____

3. They sits on the mat.

_____

E. Reading Sentences
Fill in the bubble next to the sentence that tells about each picture.

Sample	
	○ A girl sits. ○ A girl walks. ○ A girl runs.
1.	○ The boy plays ball. ○ The cat plays. ○ The girls run and play.
2.	○ The book is on the desk. ○ He has two books. ○ The pen is next to the book.
3.	○ We have a big bag. ○ She has a rabbit. ○ He has a rug and a pan.
4.	○ Six pigs sit. ○ The dog sits on a hill. ○ A pig plays in the mud.

F. Story Comprehension

Read the story. Then answer each question.
Fill in the bubble next to the best answer.

> **Pam has a dog. His name is Rags.**
>
> **Rags likes to play.**
>
> **Rags likes to run.**
>
> **Rags likes to jump.**
>
> **Rags is a good dog!**

1. What kind of pet does Pam have?
- ○ cat
- ○ dog
- ○ rabbit

2. What is a good title (name) for this story?
- ○ Rags the Dog
- ○ Frogs Jump
- ○ Apples Grow on Trees

3. What does Rags like to do?
- ○ skip
- ○ play
- ○ sing

Reading Skills Practise Test 2

A. Phonic Analysis: Consonants
Look at each picture.
Write the missing letter on the line.

Sample	**1.**	**2.**
_____at	_____ot	_____ox
3.	**4.**	**5.**
_____ell	bu_____	bu_____

B. Phonic Analysis: Vowels
Look at each picture.
Write the missing letter on the line.

Sample	**1.**	**2.**
c____p	m____p	p____g
3.	**4.**	**5.**
s____n	d____ck	t____n

C. High-Frequency Word Match

Circle the word your teacher says out loud.

Sample	1.	2.	3.	4.	5.
to	my	she	who	this	then
of	it	he	has	at	they
and	like	saw	was	that	thing

D. Vocabulary: Picture-Word Match

Fill in the bubble next to the word that names each picture.

Sample

O ham
O hat
O hot

1.

O big
O pig
O bag

2.

O ten
O top
O pot

3.

O pen
O nap
O pet

4.

O fun
O fan
O fin

5.

O sock
O tack
O cat

E. Grammar, Usage, and Mechanics

Each sentence has a mistake.
Write each sentence correctly on the blank line.

Sample the boy is happy.

_____

- -

_____

1. She saw a duck

_____

- -

_____

2. look at him run!

_____

- -

_____

3. Where will i go?

_____

- -

_____

F. Story Comprehension

Read the story. Then answer each question.
Fill in the bubble next to the best answer.

> **Ted has a pig.**
>
> **The pig's name is Big.**
>
> **Big lives in a pen.**
>
> **He plays in the mud.**
>
> **Big is a very big pig!**

1. What does Ted have?
- ○ a dog
- ○ a pig
- ○ a cat

2. What is a good title (name) for this story?
- ○ Ted's Pig
- ○ Sam's Pig
- ○ Pig Pens

3. Write a sentence telling something about Big the Pig.

_____

- -

_____

_____

- -

_____

Reading Skills Practise Test 3

A. Phonic Analysis: Consonants
Look at each picture.
Write the missing letter or letters on the line.

Sample _____un	**1.** _____all	**2.** _____ug
3. _____ag	**4.** pe_____	**5.** tru_____

B. Phonic Analysis: Vowels
Look at each picture.
Write the missing letter or letters on the line.

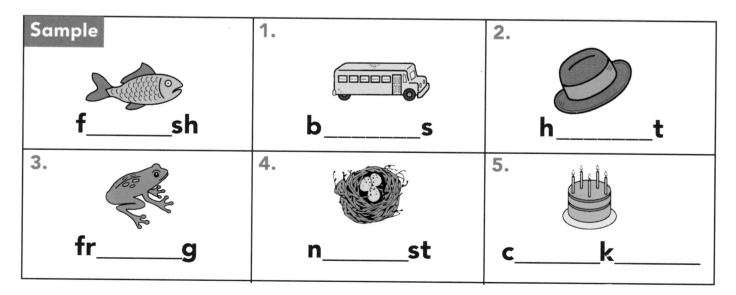

Sample f_____sh	**1.** b_____s	**2.** h_____t
3. fr_____g	**4.** n_____st	**5.** c_____k_____

C. High-Frequency Word Match
Circle the word your teacher says out loud.

Sample	1.	2.	3.	4.	5.
and	for	she	who	so	them
is	but	see	you	could	time
with	have	he	out	said	these

D. Vocabulary: Picture-Word Match
Fill in the bubble next to the word that names each picture.

Sample

○ big
○ pig
○ bird

1.

○ hat
○ bat
○ bag

2.

○ door
○ cat
○ dog

3.

○ frog
○ fan
○ feet

4.

○ hand
○ sand
○ house

5.

○ cloud
○ clock
○ sock

E. Grammar, Usage, and Mechanics
Each sentence has a mistake.
Write each sentence correctly on the line.

Sample   the girl can jump.

_____

- -

_____

1. The boy ran fast

_____

- -

_____

2. look at me!

_____

- -

_____

3. Where will i walk?

_____

- -

_____

F. Story Comprehension

Read the story. Then answer each question.
Fill in the bubble next to the best answer.

> **Kim has a kite. The kite is red. The kite has a tail. The kite flies in the sky. Kim likes her kite.**

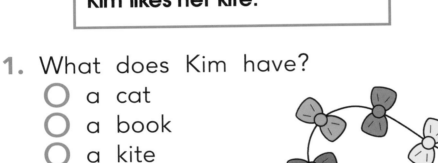

1. What does Kim have?
- ○ a cat
- ○ a book
- ○ a kite

2. What is a good title (name) for this story?
- ○ Jack's Kite
- ○ Kim's Kite
- ○ The Sky

3. Write a sentence telling something about Kim's kite.

_____

- -

_____

_____

- -

_____

Reading Skills Practise Test 4

A. Phonic Analysis: Consonants
Look at each picture.
Write the missing letter or letters on the line.

Sample	1.	2.
_____og	_____at	_____an
3.	4.	5.
_____ee	moo_____	fi_____

B. Phonic Analysis: Vowels
Look at each picture.
Write the missing letter or letters on the line.

Sample	1.	2.
s_____n	m_____p	w_____b
3.	4.	5.
f_____x	p_____g	c_____k_____

C. High-Frequency Word Match
Circle the word your teacher says out loud.

Sample	1.	2.	3.	4.	5.
and	from	she	who	can	this
at	for	see	you	could	ten
all	or	say	how	should	then

D. Vocabulary: Picture-Word Match
Fill in the bubble next to the word that names each picture.

Sample

○ ten
○ pen
○ peg

1.

○ hat
○ bat
○ ham

2.

○ fin
○ fog
○ frog

3.

○ bug
○ bus
○ bee

4.

○ feet
○ fan
○ meet

5.

○ bake
○ kite
○ bike

E. Grammar, Usage, and Mechanics

Read each sentence. Fill in the bubble next to the word or words that best complete each sentence.

Sample

_____ boy can sing.
- ○ the
- ○ The
- ○ he

1. _____ likes to swim.
- ○ She
- ○ she
- ○ the

2. _____ ride a bus.
- ○ they
- ○ They
- ○ she

3. Look _____
- ○ out?
- ○ out.
- ○ out!

4. How was your _____
- ○ day!
- ○ day?
- ○ day.

5. Her name is _____
- ○ Amy.
- ○ amy.
- ○ jen.

6. That's what _____ said.
- ○ He
- ○ I
- ○ i

7. _____ walk to school.
- ○ She
- ○ We
- ○ He

8. What is _____ name?
- ○ he
- ○ his
- ○ him

9. _____ work on a puzzle.
- ○ anna and tim
- ○ Anna and Tim
- ○ Anna

F. Story Comprehension
Read the story. Then answer each question.
Fill in the bubble next to the best answer.

> Nate has a cat. The cat's name is
> Sam. Sam is grey. Sam likes to play
> with string. Nate loves his cat!

1. What does Nate have?
- ○ a cap
- ○ a cat
- ○ a dog

2. What does Sam like to play with?
- ○ string
- ○ cats
- ○ hats

3. What is a good title for this story?
- ○ Sam's Cat
- ○ Nate's String
- ○ Nate's Cat

4. Write a sentence telling something about Nate's cat.

_____

- -

_____

_____

- -

_____

Name _____

Reading Skills Practise Test 5

A. Phonic Analysis: Consonants
Look at each picture.
Write the missing letter or letters on the line.

Sample	1.	2.
_____aby	shee_____	ba_____
3.	**4.**	**5.**
snai_____	_____ee	fro_____

B. Phonic Analysis: Vowels
Look at each picture.
Write the missing letter or letters on the line.

Sample	1.	2.
c_____r	sp_____n	l_____gs
3.	**4.**	**5.**
p_____ppies	b_____	m_____lk

C. High-Frequency Word Match
Circle the word your teacher says out loud.

Sample	1.	2.	3.	4.	5.
in	to	says	hello	big	small
is	no	said	help	bit	tall
if	go	sad	held	best	smell

D. Vocabulary: Picture-Word Match
Fill in the bubble next to the word that names each picture.

Sample

○ ant
○ plant
○ can

1.

○ pet
○ set
○ wet

2.

○ dish
○ fish
○ wish

3.

○ saw
○ paw
○ sand

4.

○ tug
○ bug
○ ball

5.

○ kite
○ cake
○ rake

E. Grammar, Usage, and Mechanics

Read each sentence. Fill in the bubble next to the word or words that best complete each sentence.

Sample   She _____ home.

- ○ is
- ○ are
- ○ Is

1. _____ read my book.

- ○ he
- ○ i
- ○ I

2. _____ plant grows.

- ○ the
- ○ The
- ○ she

3. Watch ____

- ○ me!
- ○ my.
- ○ Me!

4. _____ are going to bed.

- ○ nan and nell
- ○ Nan and Nell
- ○ Nan

5. Where do _____ live?

- ○ you
- ○ You
- ○ your

6. _____ eat some cake.

- ○ We
- ○ She
- ○ He

7. _____ get in the car.

- ○ They
- ○ they
- ○ he

8. My best friend is ____

- ○ Joey.
- ○ joey
- ○ jack.

9. _____ can play ball.

- ○ She
- ○ she
- ○ the

F. Story Comprehension
Read the story. Then answer each question.
Fill in the bubble next to the best answer.

> I have two goldfish. One fish is named Goldie. The other fish is named Finny. They are friends. I keep them in a bowl. I feed them every day.

1. What kind of pet is in this story?
- ○ cat
- ○ bird
- ○ goldfish

2. What is a good title (name) for this story?
- ○ Goldie and Finny
- ○ A Trip to the Zoo
- ○ My New Bike

3. Where do the fish in this story live?
- ○ bowl
- ○ cage
- ○ pond

Reading Skills Practise Test 6

A. Phonic Analysis: Consonants

Look at each picture.
Write the missing letter or letters on the blank line.

Sample	1.	2.
_____ag	_____op	_____eese
3. te_____	4. fi_____	5. _____ain

B. Phonic Analysis: Vowels

Look at each picture.
Write the missing letter or letters on the blank line.

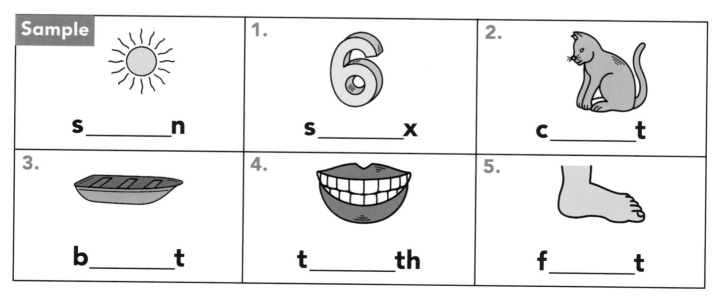

Sample	1.	2.
s_____n	s_____x	c_____t
3. b_____t	4. t_____th	5. f_____t

C. High-Frequency Word Match
Circle the word your teacher says out loud.

Sample	1.	2.	3.
he me we	as is it	saw see said	when where way

D. Grammar, Usage, and Mechanics
Each sentence has two mistakes.
Write each sentence correctly on the blank line.

Sample the dog is furry

_____

- -

_____

1. he didnt like it.

_____

- -

_____

2. can you runs fast?

_____

- -

_____

3. Where can i play

_____

- -

_____

E. Reading Sentences

Fill in the bubble next to the sentence that tells about each picture.

Sample	
	○ A boy sits. ○ A boy sleeps. ○ A boy runs.
1.	○ She wears red socks. ○ She put the rock in the box. ○ She put the sock in the box.
2.	○ The nest has six eggs. ○ The net has a fish in it. ○ The nest has ten eggs.
3.	○ She likes to swim. ○ She plays on the swing. ○ She pets the small dog.
4.	○ It rained all day. ○ The train is fast. ○ The truck can go fast.

F. Story Comprehension

Read the story. Then answer each question.
Fill in the bubble next to the best answer.

> Tom likes to read. He reads books about cats. They can climb tall trees. He reads books about dogs. They like to wag their tails. He reads books about fish. They swim in the sea. Tom reads a lot of books.

1. What does Tom like to do?
- ○ fish
- ○ read
- ○ play

2. What is a good title (name) for this story?
- ○ Good Homes for Pets
- ○ Cat and Mouse Books
- ○ Books Tom Reads

3. What does Tom read about?
- ○ school
- ○ toys
- ○ animals

4. Which book might Tom most like to read?
- ○ Fun Games to Play
- ○ Pet Rabbits
- ○ Bikes and Skates

Reading Skills Practise Test 7

A. Phonic Analysis: Consonants

Look at each picture.
Write the missing letter or letters on the blank line.

Sample	1.	2.
_____ish	_____en	_____oom
3.	**4.**	**5.**
ne_____	tru_____	_____eese

B. Phonic Analysis: Vowels

Look at each picture.
Write the missing letter or letters on the blank line.

Sample	1.	2.
b_____t	t_____n	h_____se
3.	**4.**	**5.**
l_____f	b_____k	pl_____n_____

C. High-Frequency Word Match
Circle the word your teacher says out loud.

Sample	1.	2.	3.
in and are	hat his has	some come could	wet where what

D. Grammar, Usage, and Mechanics
Each sentence has two mistakes.
Write each sentence correctly on the blank line.

Sample the cat sleeps

_____

_____

1. why cant we go?

_____

_____

2. They plays all day

_____

_____

3. Can sam sit with us

_____

_____

E. Reading Sentences

Fill in the bubble next to the sentence
that tells about each picture.

Sample	
	◯ The boy hits the ball. ◯ The boy kicks the ball. ◯ The boy throws the ball.
1.	◯ The duck sits on a rock. ◯ The dog runs by the lake. ◯ The duck swims in the pond.
2.	◯ She rides her bike. ◯ The girl has a big kite. ◯ They have a new bike.
3.	◯ The branch has five leaves. ◯ The tree has no leaves. ◯ The leaf fell off the branch.
4.	◯ He sits next to the cow. ◯ He can see the cow. ◯ He is near a horse.

F. Story Comprehension

Read the story. Then answer each question.
Fill in the bubble next to the best answer.

> The wind helps people. The wind helps people to fly kites. The wind also helps people to sail boats. The wind helps plants, too. The wind blows plant seeds to new places. Soon, the seeds grow. Then there are new plants.

1. What is a good title (name) for this story?
○ How to Sail a Boat
○ The Wind
○ Growing Plants

2. How does the wind help people?
○ to fly a kite
○ to make a book
○ to make a boat

3. What happens after the wind blows plant seeds?
○ rocks grow
○ seeds grow
○ people grow

4. What other thing do you think the wind can do?
○ make a kite
○ blow away a leaf
○ be a home for animals

Reading Skills Practise Test 8

A. Phonic Analysis: Consonants

Look at each picture.
Write the missing letter or letters on the line.

Sample	1.	2.
_____esk	_____an	_____ee
3.	**4.**	**5.**
_____ip	clo_____	ha_____

B. Phonic Analysis: Vowels

Look at each picture.
Write the missing letter or letters on the line.

Sample	1.	2.
n_____t	c_____p	m_____n
3.	**4.**	**5.**
cl_____d	b_____t	r_____k_____

C. Vocabulary: Picture-Word Match

Fill in the bubble next to the word that names each picture.

Sample	1.	2.
○ fast ○ fish ○ first	○ bad ○ bed ○ bet	○ net ○ fast ○ nest
3.	**4.**	**5.**
○ plane ○ pan ○ plate	○ cot ○ coat ○ cap	○ bike ○ kit ○ kite

D. High-Frequency Word Match

Circle the word your teacher says out loud.

Sample	1.	2.	3.	4.	5.
it in out	him he his	when they then	said says say	are our your	who was what

E. Grammar, Usage, and Mechanics

Each sentence has two mistakes.
Write each sentence correctly on the blank line.

Sample he ride in a plane.

_____

- -

_____

1. she runs very fast

_____

- -

_____

2. where are my socks

_____

- -

_____

3. We plays with the dog

_____

- -

_____

F. Story Comprehension

Read the story. Then answer each question.
Fill in the bubble next to the best answer.

> Have you ever seen a rabbit? Rabbits come in many colours. Their fur can be brown, black, white, or grey. Rabbits have long ears to help them hear sounds from far away.
>
> Rabbits can be wild animals or pets. Wild rabbits live in holes in the ground. Pet rabbits live in homes with people.

1. What is a good title (name) for this story?
   ○ Colours
   ○ Rabbits
   ○ Wild Animals

2. What do a rabbit's long ears help it to do?
   ○ hear sounds from far away
   ○ make holes in the ground
   ○ see things that are far away

3. Where are two places rabbits can live?
   ○ on land and in the sea
   ○ in holes in the ground and in people's homes
   ○ in people's homes and in treetops

4. Write a sentence telling something about rabbits.

   _____

   _____

   _____

   _____

Reading Skills Practise Test 9

A. Phonic Analysis: Consonants
Look at each picture.
Write the missing letters on the line.

Sample	1.	2.
_____ess	_____ain	_____ag
3.	4.	5.
la_____	de_____	_____oon

B. Phonic Analysis: Vowels
Look at each picture.
Write the missing letter or letters on the line.

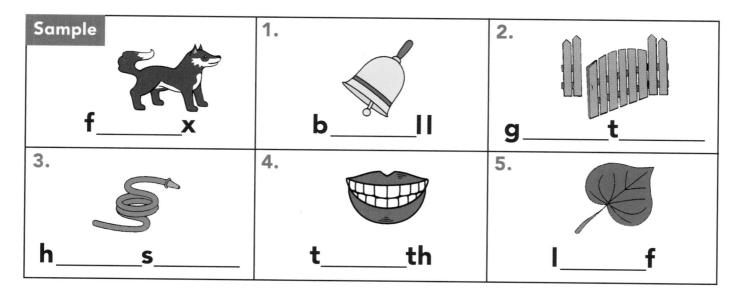

Sample	1.	2.
f_____x	b_____ll	g_____t_____
3.	4.	5.
h_____s_____	t_____th	l_____f

C. High-Frequency Word Match

Fill in the bubble next to the word your teacher says out loud.

Sample	1.	2.	3.	4.	5.
○ him	○ very	○ small	○ true	○ which	○ between
○ her	○ vine	○ song	○ that	○ what	○ because
○ house	○ cherry	○ some	○ there	○ where	○ bacon

D. Vocabulary: Picture-Word Match

Fill in the bubble next to the word that names each picture.

Sample

○ fly
○ hog
○ frog

1.

○ key
○ kite
○ cake

2.

○ fast
○ fig
○ fish

3.

○ plane
○ pond
○ plum

4.

○ carrot
○ cupcake
○ cup

5.

○ butterfly
○ butter
○ button

E. Grammar, Usage, and Mechanics

Read each sentence. Fill in the bubble next to the word or words that best complete each sentence.

Sample

_____ walk to school.
- ○ we
- ○ look
- ○ We

1. My kitten likes to _____
- ○ jump.
- ○ jump?
- ○ Jump

2. I went to see _____ for a checkup.
- ○ dr. Jones
- ○ Dr. Jones
- ○ dr. jones

3. May _____ play with you?
- ○ i
- ○ It
- ○ I

4. My family went to _____ on a trip.
- ○ New Brunswick
- ○ NEW BRUNSWICK
- ○ new brunswick

5. The girl _____ the bus.
- ○ ride
- ○ rides
- ○ rided

F. Story Comprehension

Read the story. Then answer each question.
Fill in the bubble next to the best answer.

Jane Goodall

Jane Goodall is a famous scientist. She learned about wild chimpanzees in Africa.

Jane learned that baby chimpanzees ride on their mothers' backs until they are 3 years old. She learned that chimpanzees hold hands like people do. She also learned that chimpanzees use sticks to catch insects. Jane learned all about chimpanzees by watching them closely.

1. What is a good title for this story?
- ○ Scientists
- ○ Jane Goodall
- ○ Baby Chimpanzees

2. Where did Jane Goodall learn about chimpanzees?
- ○ Africa
- ○ South America
- ○ Asia

3. Baby chimpanzees ride on their mothers' backs until what age?
- ○ 5 years old
- ○ 6 months old
- ○ 3 years old

4. Write a sentence telling something that Jane Goodall learned about chimpanzees.

_____

_____

_____

Reading Skills Practise Test 10

A. Phonic Analysis: Consonants

Look at each picture.
Write the missing letter or letters on the blank line.

Sample	1.	2.
_____og	_____ix	_____ee
3.	4.	5.
to _____	fa_____	_____ip

B. Phonic Analysis: Vowels

Look at each picture.
Write the missing letter or letters on the blank line.

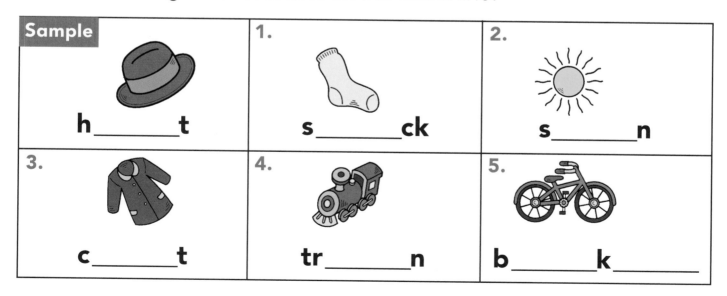

Sample	1.	2.
h_____t	s_____ck	s_____n
3.	4.	5.
c_____t	tr_____n	b_____k_____

C. High-Frequency Word Match
Circle the word your teacher says out loud.

Sample	1.	2.	3.
the	as	had	see
me	is	has	sad
to	it	have	said

D. Grammar, Usage, and Mechanics
Each sentence has two mistakes.
Write each sentence correctly on the blank line.

Sample the boy is happy

_____

_____

1. she cant help us.

_____

_____

2. can we plays ball?

_____

_____

3. Where will i go

_____

_____

E. Reading Sentences

Fill in the bubble next to the sentence that tells about each picture.

Sample	
	○ A girl sits. ○ A girl sleeps. ○ A girl runs.
1.	○ He pets the cat. ○ He walks the dog. ○ He sits on the rock.
2.	○ I can see the nest. ○ I can sit next to you. ○ I can zip up my coat.
3.	○ The man has a big hat. ○ The man has six hats. ○ The man has to hop.
4.	○ I like to bake cakes. ○ I like to play games. ○ I like to ride my bike.

F. Story Comprehension

Read the story. Then answer each question.
Fill in the bubble next to the best answer.

> Cats and dogs are good pets. You can find these pets in many homes. A cat is a good pet. A cat can run and jump. A cat can play with a ball of yarn. A cat can also lick your hand.
>
> A dog is a good pet, too. A dog can chase after a ball. A dog can jump up and catch a stick. A dog can also help keep you safe.

1. What two animals make good pets?
- ○ cats
- ○ dogs and sharks
- ○ dogs and cats

2. What is a good title (name) for this story?
- ○ Good Pets
- ○ Cats at Home
- ○ Pet Food

3. What can both cats and dogs do?
- ○ jump up and catch a stick
- ○ keep you safe
- ○ run and jump

Reading Skills Practise Test 11

A. Phonic Analysis: Consonants

Look at each picture.
Write the missing letters on the line.

Sample	1.	2.
_____oor	_____ant	_____elve
3.	**4.**	**5.**
_____umb	_____eakers	ben_____

B. Phonic Analysis: Vowels

Look at each picture.
Write the missing letter or letters on the line.

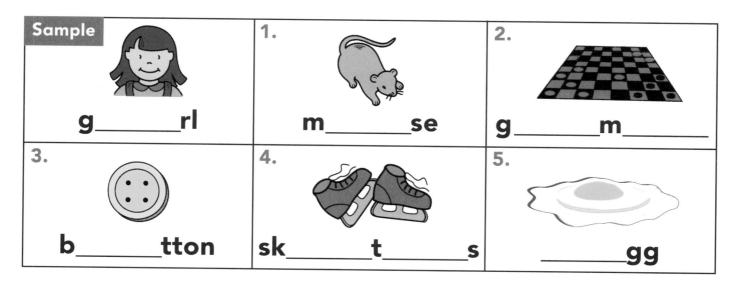

Sample	1.	2.
g_____rl	m_____se	g_____m_____
3.	**4.**	**5.**
b_____tton	sk_____t_____s	_____gg

C. High-Frequency Word Match

Fill in the bubble next to the word your teacher says out loud.

Sample	1.	2.	3.	4.	5.
○ sad ○ said ○ send	○ fat ○ fit ○ that	○ like ○ lick ○ luck	○ sit ○ sat ○ set	○ up ○ on ○ of	○ black ○ book ○ blue

D. Vocabulary: Picture-Word Match

Fill in the bubble next to the word that names each picture.

Sample	1.	2.
○ jump ○ gum ○ jam	○ brush ○ bush ○ bird	○ fins ○ fence ○ friends

3.	4.	5.
○ pants ○ pins ○ ants	○ bill ○ doll ○ bell	○ next ○ nine ○ mine

E. Grammar, Usage, and Mechanics

Read each sentence. Fill in the bubble next to the word or words that best complete each sentence.

Sample

The cat _____ its food.
- ○ eat
- ○ eats
- ○ Eats

1. _____ teacher is nice.
- ○ My
- ○ my
- ○ me

2. Grandma _____ in a house.
- ○ live
- ○ Lives
- ○ lives

3. Careful! The fire _____ hot.
- ○ are
- ○ is
- ○ Is

4. _____ you like ice cream?
- ○ does
- ○ Does
- ○ Do

5. I _____ a loose tooth.
- ○ have
- ○ Have
- ○ has

6. _____ eat some cake.
- ○ They
- ○ Him
- ○ Her

F. Story Comprehension

Read the story. Then answer each question.
Fill in the bubble next to the best answer.

> Baby penguins come from eggs. When a penguin is ready to be born, it starts to peck the shell. The shell is thick. It can take three days to get out! When the penguin is born, it has soft fluff all over. Its eyes are shut. It peeps to be fed! The mother and father take turns feeding and caring for their chick.

1. What is a good title for this story?
○ Baby Penguins
○ Penguins
○ Eggs

2. How long can it take for a baby penguin to peck out of its shell?
○ one day
○ two days
○ three days

3. Who takes care of a baby penguin?
○ the mother
○ the father
○ the mother and father

4. Write a sentence that tells something about baby penguins.

_____
- -

_____
- -

_____

Scholastic Success With

TRADITIONAL MANUSCRIPT

Name _____

A a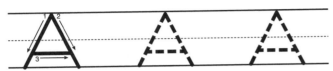

Trace and write.

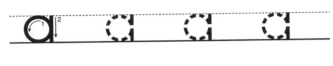

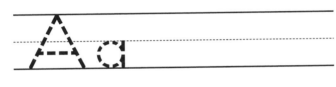

Adam Ape is active.

Annie asked Alice.

Bb

Trace and write.

B   B   B   B

b   b   b   b

Bb

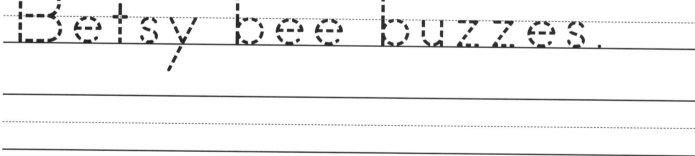

Betsy bee buzzes.

Bobby buys balloons.

Cc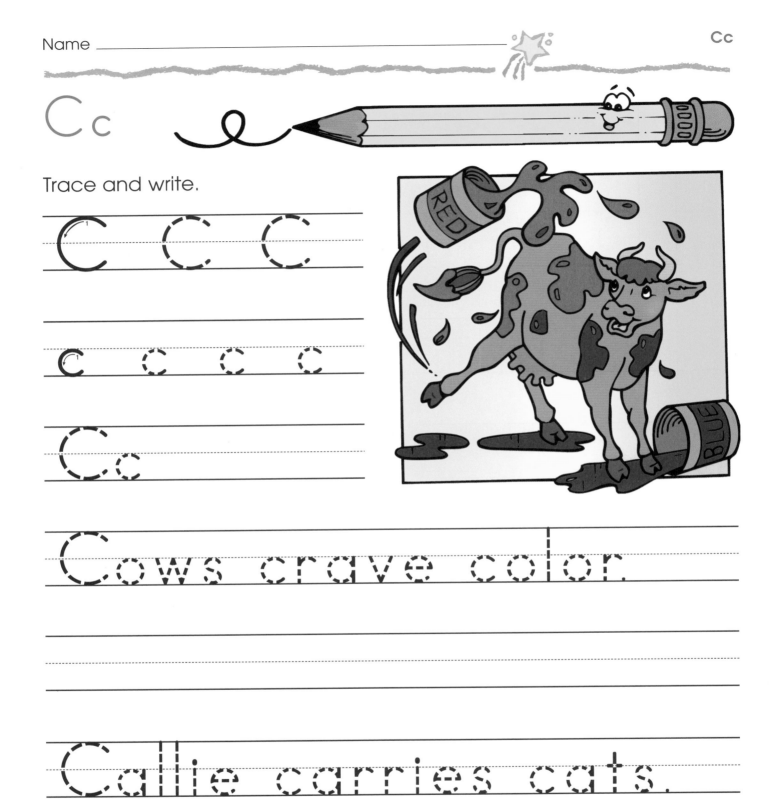

Trace and write.

C   C   C   C

c   c   c   c

Cc

Cows crave color.

Callie carries cats.

D d

Trace and write.

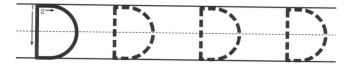

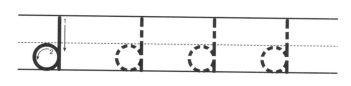

Dandy Duck dances.

Dragons draw dogs.

Ee

Trace and write.

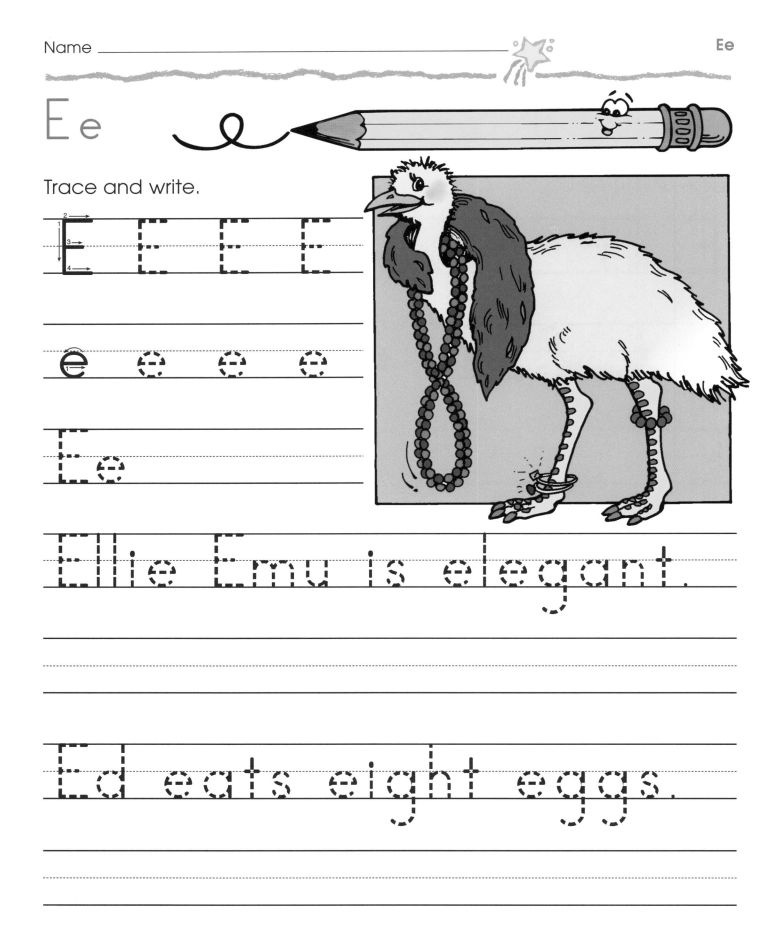

E E E E E

e e e e

E e

Ellie Emu is elegant.

Ed eats eight eggs.

Ff

F f

Trace and write.

F

f

Ff

Fran Fish is funny.

Footballs fly fast.

G g

Trace and write.

G G G

g g g g

Gg

Hee Hee Hee

Gus Goose giggles.

Greta grows greens.

Hh

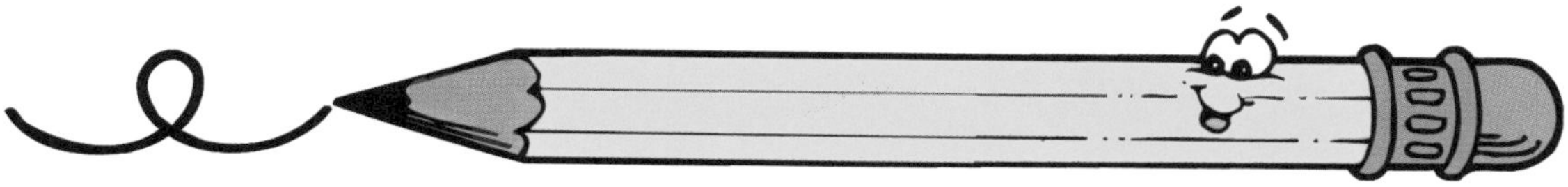

Trace and write.

H H H H

h h h h

Hh

Ha! Hippo is happy.

Hannah hangs hats.

Ii

Trace and write.

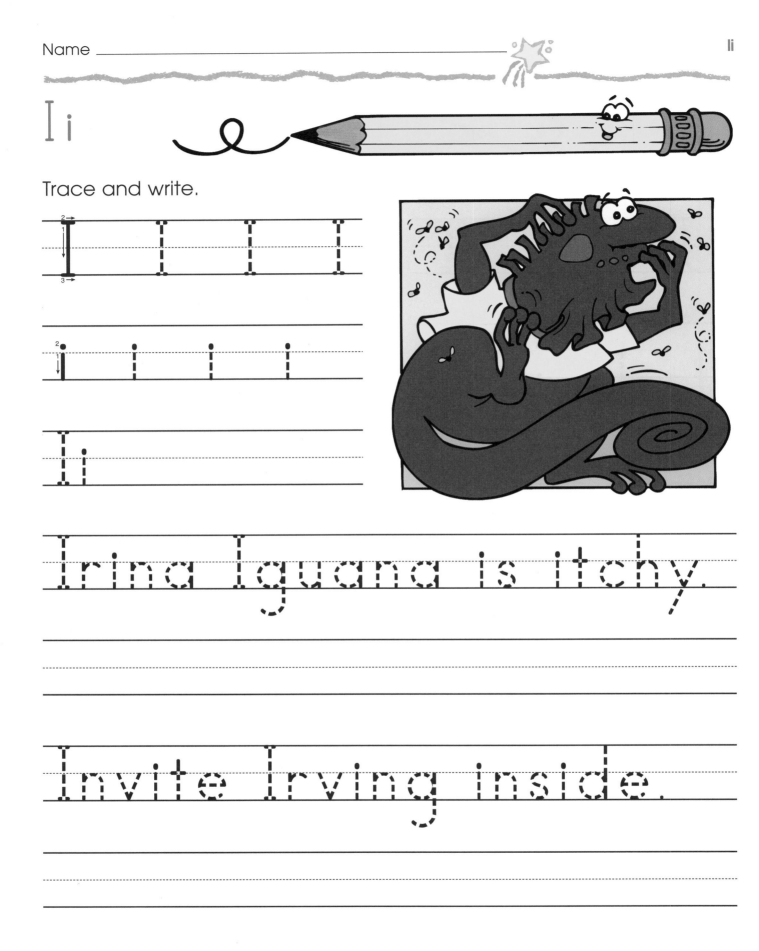

I I I I I

i i i i i

Ii

Irina Iguana is itchy.

Invite Irving inside.

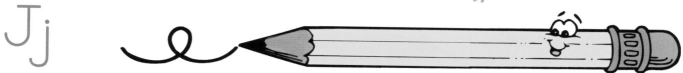

Jj

Trace and write.

J J J

J J J J

Jj

Jim Jellyfish is jazzy.

Jill juggles jelly jars.

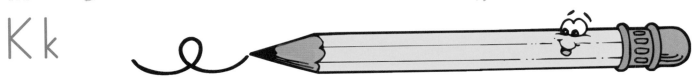

K k

Trace and write.

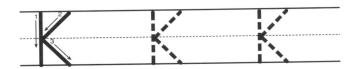

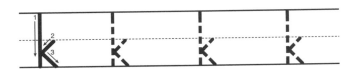

Kyle Kangaroo kicks.

Katie keeps kittens.

Name ______________________________

Ll

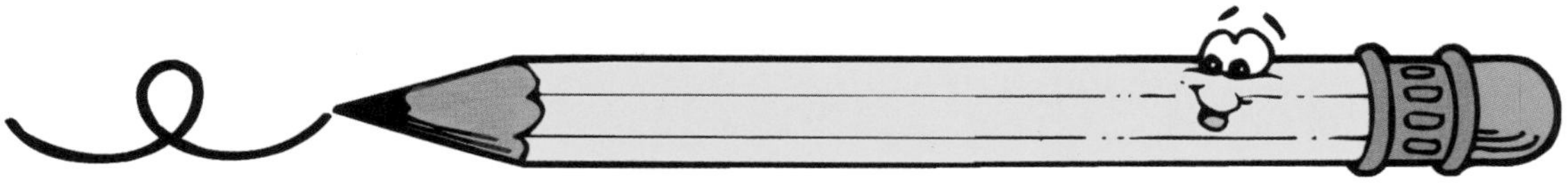

Trace and write.

L L L L

l l l l l

L l

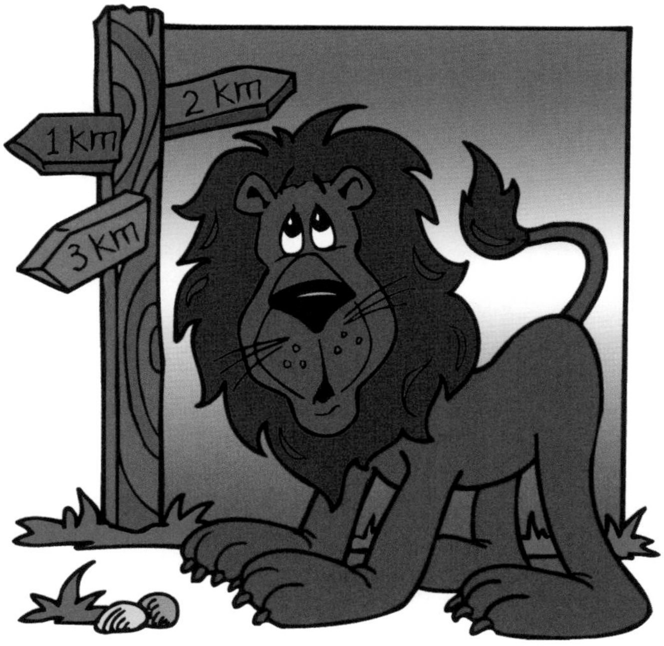

Lyle Lion looks lost.

Lindy loves lollipops.

Mm

Trace and write.

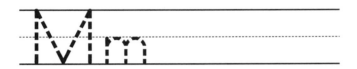

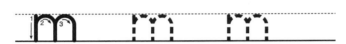

Mike Mouse is messy.

Mom met Madeline.

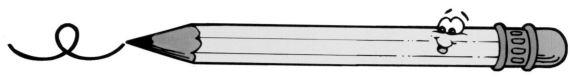

N n

Trace and write.

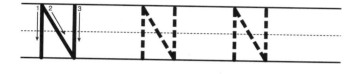

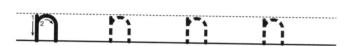

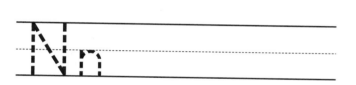

Nikki Newt needs naps.

Nurse Ned nibbles.

Name _____

O o

Trace and write.

O O O

O O O O

O o

Opal Owl sings opera.

Otis orders oranges.

Name ______________________________

P p

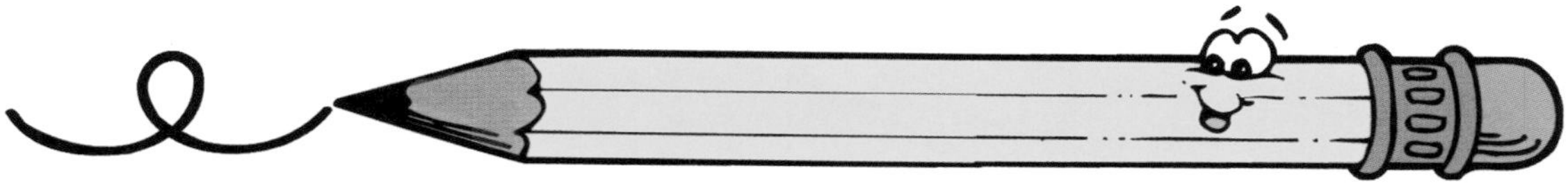

Trace and write.

P P P

p p p p

Pp

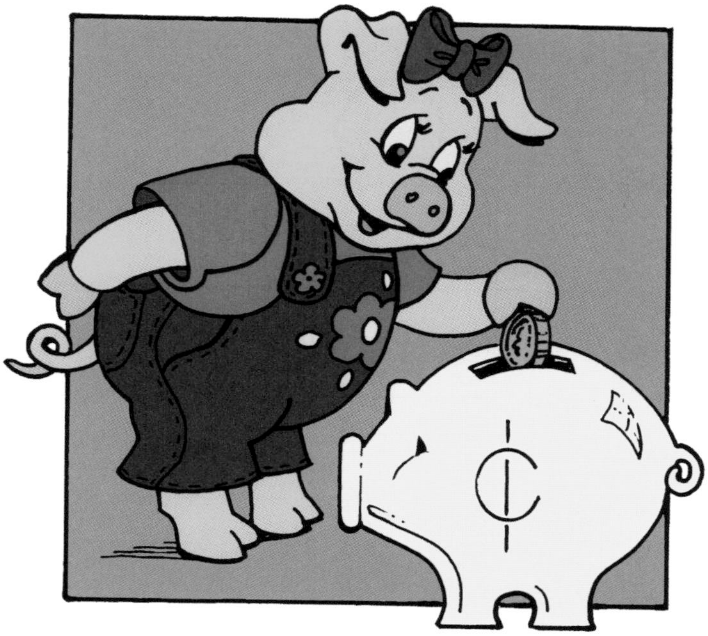

Pam Pig paid a penny.

Peter Pig says please.

Name _____

Q q

Trace and write.

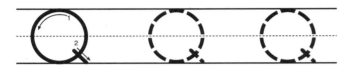

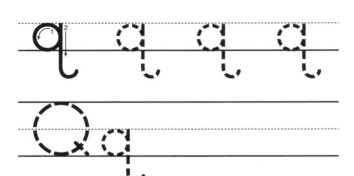

shhhh!

Quinn Quail is quiet.

Quebec is quite nice.

Name _____

R r

Trace and write.

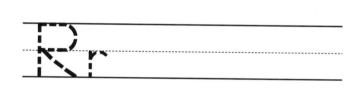

Randy Rabbit races.

Robin reads rapidly.

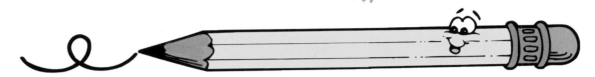
S s

Trace and write.

S S S S

s s s s

Ss

Susanna Seal stars.

Sam sees sailboats.

Name _____

Tt

Tt

Trace and write.

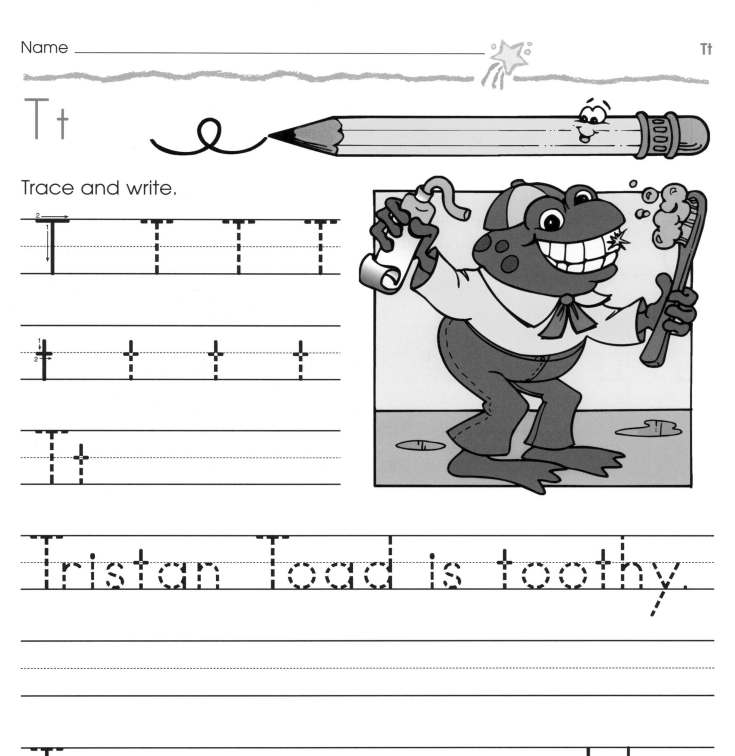

T T T T

t t t t

Tt

Tristan Toad is toothy.

Tigers taste terrible.

U u

Trace and write.

U U U U

u u u u

Uu

Ula uses an umbrella.

Uncle Uno umpires.

V v

Trace and write.

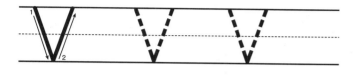

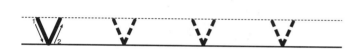

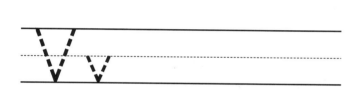

Vic Vulture is vain.

Vegetables vary.

Name _____

W w

Trace and write.

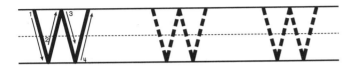

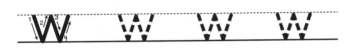

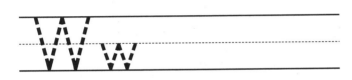

Will Worm is wealthy.

Wilma wipes windows.

X x

Trace and write.

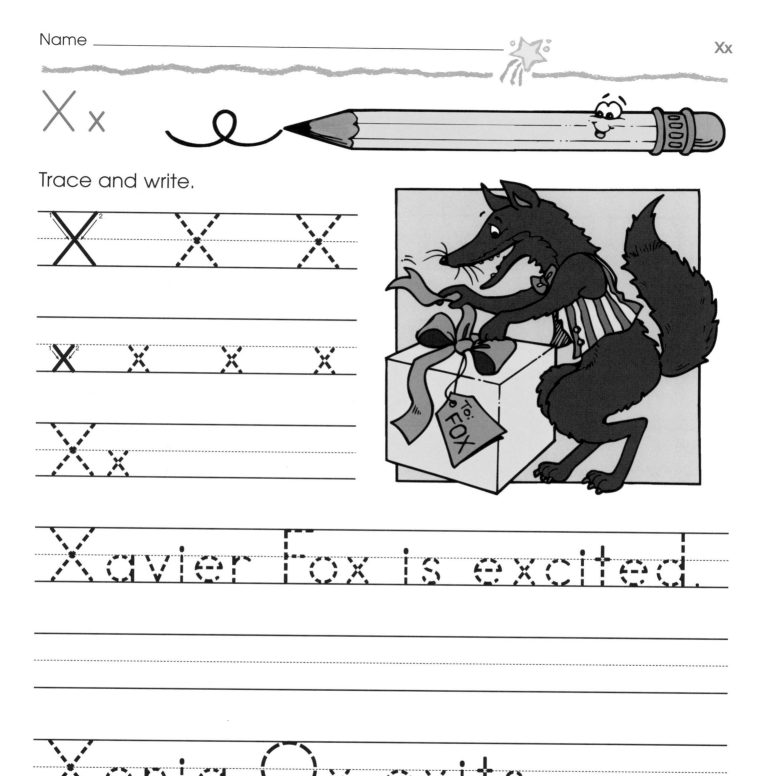

X X X

X X X X

X x

Xavier Fox is excited.

Xenia Ox exits.

Yy

Trace and write.

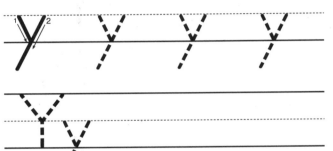

Y   Y   Y

y   y   y   y   y

Yy

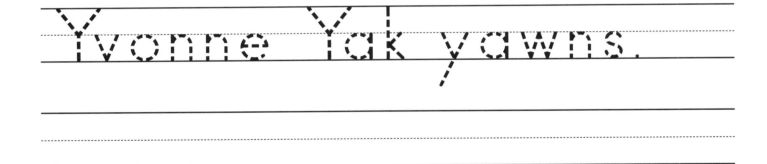

Yvonne Yak yawns.

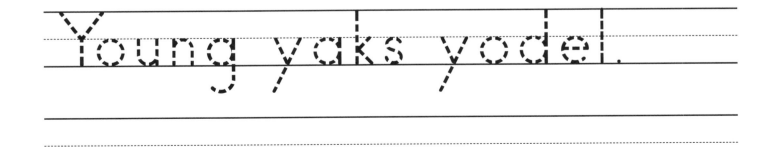

Young yaks yodel.

Z z

Trace and write.

Zoe Zebra is zany.

Zed zooms at the zoo.

A–Z

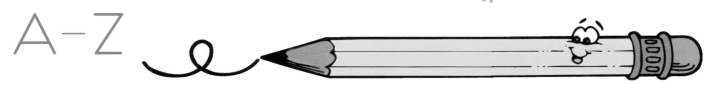

Trace and write.

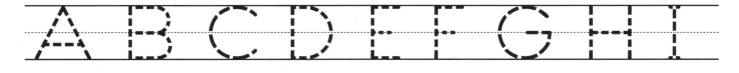

A B C D E F G H I

J K L M N O P Q

R S T U V W X Y Z

a – z

Trace and write.

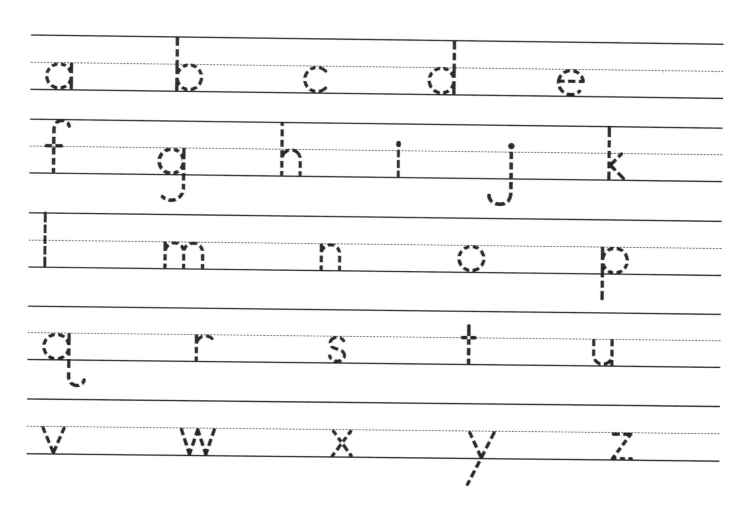

a   b   c   d   e

f   g   h   i   j   k

l   m   n   o   p

q   r   s   t   u

v   w   x   y   z

abcd

1-5

Trace and write.

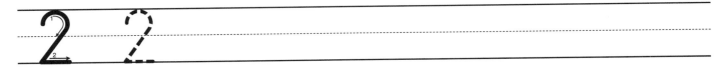

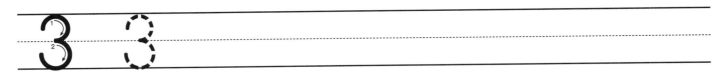

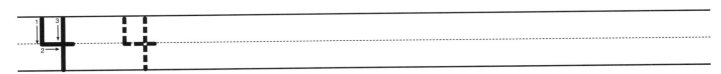

6-10

Trace and write.

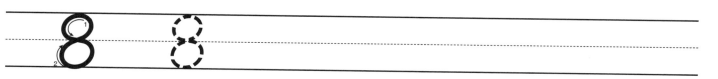

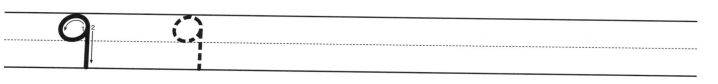

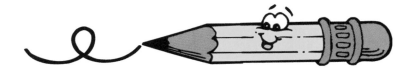

Colour Words

Trace and write.

red

yellow

blue

green

orange

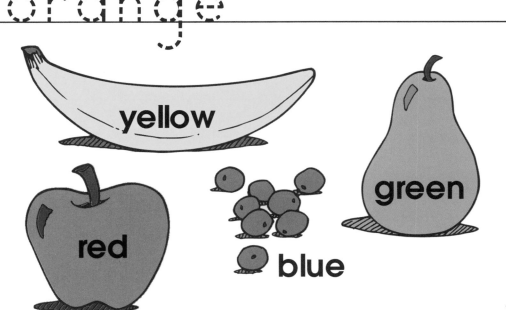

yellow

red

blue

green

orange

More Colour Words

Trace and write.

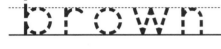

purple

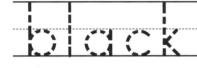

brown

black

white

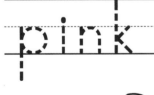

pink

pink

white

brown

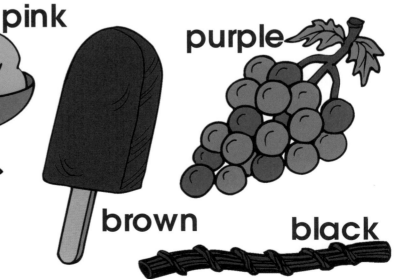

purple

black

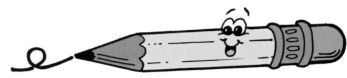

Name _____

Number Words

Trace and write.

one

two

three

four

five

1 one

2 two

3 three

4 four

5 five

More Number Words

Trace and write.

6 six

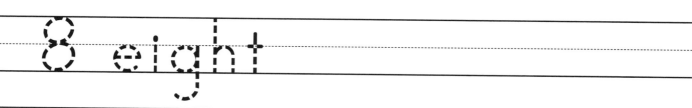

7 seven

8 eight

9 nine

10 ten

Name _____

Shapes

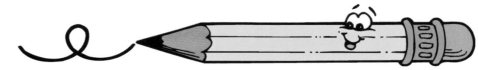

Trace and write.

oval

heart

circle

square

triangle

diamond

rectangle

Days of the Week

Trace and write.

Sunday _____

Monday _____

Tuesday _____

Wednesday _____

Thursday _____

Friday _____

Saturday _____

Months

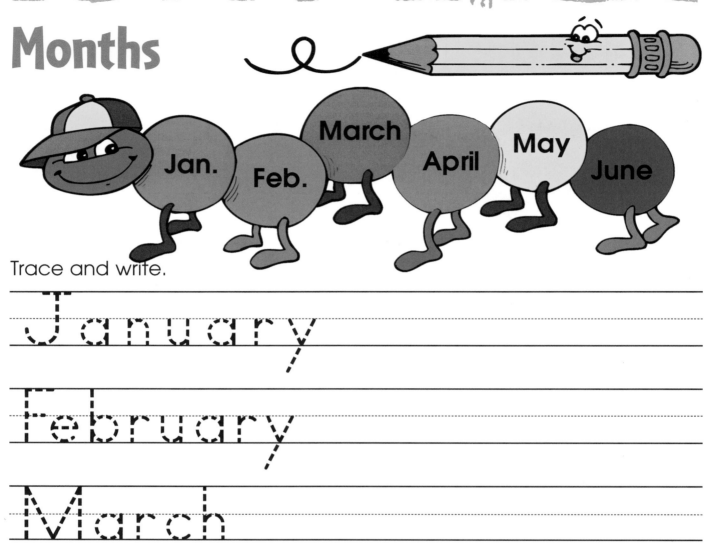

Trace and write.

January

February

March

April

May

June

Months

Trace and write.

July

August

September

October

November

December

Special Days

Write each special day.

New Year's Day _____
_____
_____

Valentine's Day _____
_____
_____

St. Patrick's Day _____
_____
_____

Mother's Day _____
_____
_____

Father's Day _____
_____
_____

Canada Day _____
_____
_____

Special Days

Write each special day.

AUG   SEPT.   OCT   NOV.   DEC.

Labour Day

_____

- - - - - - - - - - - - - - - - - - -

_____

Halloween

_____

- - - - - - - - - - - - - - - - - - -

_____

Thanksgiving

_____

- - - - - - - - - - - - - - - - - - -

_____

Hannukah

_____

- - - - - - - - - - - - - - - - - - -

_____

Christmas

_____

- - - - - - - - - - - - - - - - - - -

_____

Kwanzaa

_____

- - - - - - - - - - - - - - - - - - -

_____

Animals From A to Z

Write the animal names on the
lines below.

alligator
bear
cougar
duck

elk
frog
giraffe
horse

iguana
jaguar
kangaroo
leopard

moose
newt
ostrich

Animals From A to Z

Write the animal names on the
lines below.

parrot
quail
raccoon

squirrel
tiger
urchin

vulture
whale
X-ray fish

yak
zebra

Name _____

The Continents

Write the names of the continents.

Africa
_____
- -
_____

Asia
_____
- -
_____

Australia
_____
- -
_____

Antarctica
_____
- -
_____

Europe
_____
- -
_____

North America
_____
- -
_____

South America
_____
- -
_____

Africa

Asia

Antarctica

Australia

Europe

North America

South America

The Planets

Write the names of the planets.

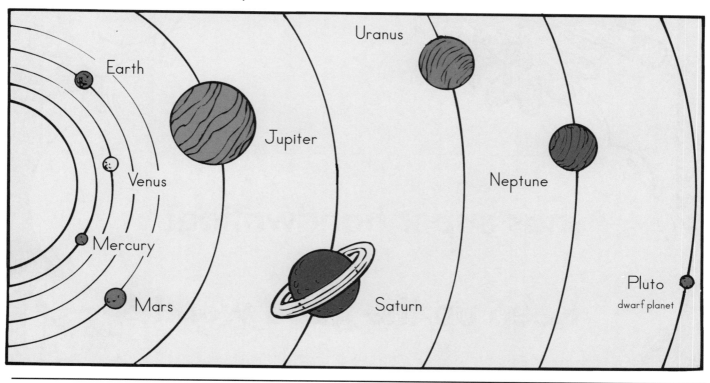

Earth

Uranus

Jupiter

Venus

Neptune

Mercury

Mars

Saturn

Pluto
dwarf planet

has super handwriting!

Keep up the good work!

_____
signed

_____
date

Scholastic Success With

GRAMMAR

Capitalizing First Word

 A sentence always begins with a capital letter.

Draw a line under the first letter in each sentence.
Read each sentence to a friend.

1 **The cat sat on a rat.**

2 **The rat sat on a hat.**

3 **The hat is on the dog.**

4 **The dog is on a mat.**

Capitalizing First Word

 A sentence always begins with a capital letter.

Copy each sentence correctly on the line.

1 the cat sat.

_____

- -

_____

2 the dog sat.

_____

- -

_____

3 i see the cat.

_____

- -

_____

4 i can see.

_____

- -

_____

Capitalizing First Word

Read each sentence. Then fill in the circle next to the word with the capital letter that begins the sentence.

1 The cat is in the van.
- ○ cat
- ○ The

2 My dog can run.
- ○ My
- ○ dog

3 Jan can hop.
- ○ Jan
- ○ hop

4 I like ham.
- ○ ham
- ○ I

5 Ants like jam.
- ○ jam
- ○ Ants

Periods

A telling sentence ends with a period.

Circle the period at the end of each sentence.

1 **I see Jan.**

2 **I go with Jan.**

3 **We see Dan.**

4 **I go with Dan and Jan.**

Draw a line under the last word in each sentence.
Add a period to each sentence.

5 **We go to school**

6 **We like school**

Periods

 A telling sentence ends with a period.

Write a period where it belongs in each sentence. Read the sentences to a friend.

1 Dan is in the cab

2 The cat is in the cab

3 Mom is in the cab

4 We see Dan and Mom

Read the words. Write each word at the end of the correct sentence.

van.   red.

5 We can go in the _____

6 The van is _____

Periods

Read each group of words. Fill in the circle next to the correct sentence.

1
- ◯ The cat is on the mat.
- ◯ the cat is on the mat
- ◯ the cat on the mat

2
- ◯ the rat is on the mop
- ◯ the rat is on the mop
- ◯ The rat is on the mop.

3
- ◯ The rat sees the cat
- ◯ The rat sees the cat.
- ◯ the rat sees the cat

4
- ◯ The rat can hop.
- ◯ The rat can hop
- ◯ the rat can hop

5
- ◯ the cat and rat sit
- ◯ The cat and rat sit
- ◯ The cat and rat sit.

Capitalizing I

 Always write the word I with a capital letter.

Circle the word **I** in each sentence.

1 I like to hop.   **2** Pam and I like to hop.

3 I can hop to Mom.   **4** Mom and I can hop.

Draw what you like. Use the word **I** to write about it.

5 _____

Capitalizing I

 Always write the word I with a capital letter.

Read the sentences. Write **I** on the line.

1 _____ will ride.

2 _____ will swim.

3 Mom and _____ will sing.

4 Then _____ will read.

What will you do next? Write it on the line.

5 ___ I will _____

Capitalizing I

Read each group of words. Fill in the circle next to the correct sentence.

1

◯ i sit on a mat.

◯ I sit on a mat.

◯ i sit on a mat

2

◯ Pam and I like cats.

◯ Pam and i like cats.

◯ pam and i like cats

3

◯ I see the van.

◯ i see the van.

◯ i see the van

4

◯ i like jam.

◯ i like jam

◯ I like jam.

5

◯ i like to nap.

◯ I like to nap.

◯ i like to nap

Simple Sentences

 A sentence tells a complete idea.

Circle who or what each sentence is about.

1 **Pam ran.**

2 **Dan hops.**

3 **The cat sits.**

4 **The van can go.**

Draw a line from each sentence to the picture
of who or what the sentence is about.

5 **Jan is hot.**

6 **The hat is on top.**

7 **The man sat.**

Name _____

Simple Sentences

 A sentence tells a complete idea.

Circle each sentence.

1 **Bill**
Bill paints.

2 **likes to read**
Tom likes to read.

3 **plants flowers**
Pat plants flowers.

Finish the sentence.

4 I like

Simple Sentences

Read each group of words. Fill in the circle next to the complete sentence.

1

◯ on a mat

◯ The cat sits on a mat.

◯ The cat

2

◯ Pam and Dan like jam.

◯ Pam and Dan

◯ like jam

3

◯ I see Mom.

◯ I see

◯ Mom

4

◯ my hat

◯ I like

◯ I like my hat.

5

◯ Ben.

◯ Ben can hop.

◯ hop

Word Order

 Words in a sentence must be in an order that makes sense.

Read each group of words. Draw a line under the word that should go first in each sentence.

1 dots. I like   **2** Pam dots. likes

3 like We hats.   **4** hats with dots. We like

Now write each group of words in the right order.

1 _____

2 _____

3 _____

4 _____

Word Order

Words in a sentence must be in an order that makes sense.

Read each group of words. Write them in the right order on the lines.

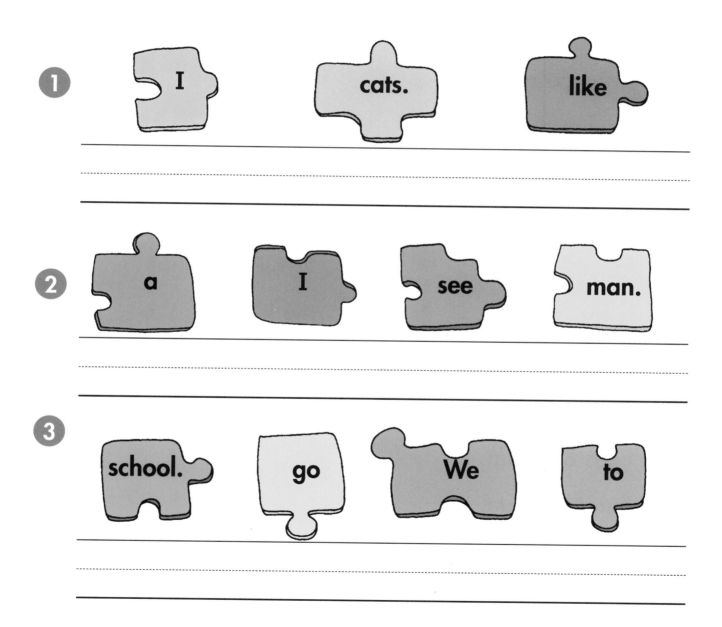

1 I   cats.   like

_____

- -

_____

2 a   I   see   man.

_____

- -

_____

3 school.   go   We   to

_____

- -

_____

Remember: A sentence begins with a capital letter. A telling sentence ends with a period.

Word Order

Read each group of words. Fill in the circle next to the words that are in an order that makes sense.

1
- ⬭ I red dots. see
- ⬭ I see red dots.
- ⬭ dots red

2
- ⬭ Dan is in a big van.
- ⬭ big Dan a van. is in
- ⬭ van big Dan in a is

3
- ⬭ fat. cat The is
- ⬭ is fat. The cat
- ⬭ The cat is fat.

4
- ⬭ We like the hat.
- ⬭ the like hat. We
- ⬭ We hat. the like

5
- ⬭ likes Ben jam.
- ⬭ Ben likes jam.
- ⬭ jam. likes Ben

Question Sentences

Question sentences ask something.

Read each sentence. Circle each question mark.

1 **Who hid the hat?**

2 **Is it on the cat?**

3 **Can you see the hat?**

4 **Is it on the man?**

Write two questions. Draw a line under each capital letter at the beginning of each question. Circle the question marks.

5 _____

_____

6 _____

_____

Question Sentences

 Question sentences ask something.

Draw a line under each sentence that asks a question.
Circle the question mark.

1 Who hid the cat?

2 Can the cat see the rat?

3 The cat is in the van.

4 Can the van go?

Read the sentences. Circle each sentence that asks something.

5 Can we sit in the van?

  We can sit in the van.

6 Dan can nap in the van.

  Can Dan nap in the van?

Question Sentences

Read the sentences. Fill in the circle next to the sentence that asks a question.

1

- ⬭ Who hid my hat?
- ⬭ My hat is with him.
- ⬭ My hat is big.

2

- ⬭ The hat has spots.
- ⬭ The hat has dots.
- ⬭ Did the hat have dots?

3

- ⬭ Jan likes my hat.
- ⬭ Did Jan like my hat?
- ⬭ Jan did like my hat.

4

- ⬭ Can you see the hat?
- ⬭ You can see the hat.
- ⬭ She can see the hat.

5

- ⬭ Dan can get a hat.
- ⬭ Dan likes hats.
- ⬭ Dan has the hat?

Naming Words

A naming word names a person, place, or thing.

Read each sentence. Draw a line under the word or words that name the person, place, or thing in each sentence.

1 **The pig is big.**

2 **The pan is hot.**

3 **Pam hid.**

4 **Can you run up the hill?**

Draw a line from each sentence to the picture that shows the naming word in that sentence.

5 **The sun is hot.**

6 **Sam ran and ran.**

7 **Is the cat fat?**

Naming Words

A naming word names a person, place, or thing.

Circle the naming words in the sentences.

1 **Al can go in a van.**

2 **The cat sat on a mat.**

3 **Pat ran up the hill.**

4 **Dan and Jan will mop.**

Draw a picture of a person, place, or thing. Write a sentence about your picture. Circle the naming word.

_____

_____

Naming Words

Read each sentence. Fill in the circle next to the naming word.

1 **I see a big cat.**

(a) see   (b) big   (c) cat

2 **The rat ran fast.**

(a) ran   (b) rat   (c) fast

3 **Can you see the map?**

(a) Can   (b) map   (c) see

4 **The van is tan.**

(a) van   (b) is   (c) tan

5 **The fan is not on!**

(a) not   (b) on   (c) fan

Capitalizing Special Names

 The names of people, places, and pets are special. They begin with capital letters.

Draw a line under the special name in each sentence. Then circle the first letter or letters in that name.

1 They go to Hill Park.

2 Pam sees the ham.

3 Don sees the cat.

4 They like Frog Lake

Write a special name of a person, place, or pet you know.

5 _____

Capitalizing Special Names

 The names of people, places, and pets are special. They begin with capital letters.

Circle each special name. Draw a line under each capital letter in each name.

1 I am Pam.

2 I sit on Ant Hill.

3 Ron likes the lake.

4 He likes Bat Lake.

Read the special names in the box.
Write a special name for each picture.

| Spot   Hill Street |

5

6

Capitalizing Special Names

Read each sentence. Fill in the circle next to the special name.

1 **Can Don go to the picnic?**

- ⬭ picnic
- ⬭ Don
- ⬭ Can

2 **The picnic will be on Pig Hill.**

- ⬭ Pig Hill
- ⬭ picnic
- ⬭ The

3 **The hill is on Jam Street.**

- ⬭ hill
- ⬭ The
- ⬭ Jam Street

4 **Jan will go to the picnic.**

- ⬭ go
- ⬭ picnic
- ⬭ Jan

5 **She will go in Ham Lake.**

- ⬭ She
- ⬭ Ham Lake
- ⬭ will

Action Words

An action word tells what happens.

Read each sentence. Circle the word that tells what happens.

1 **The hen sits.**

2 **The cat ran.**

3 **Pam hid.**

4 **The dog naps.**

Read the words. Use the words to finish the sentences.

| run | see |

_____

- -

5 **I will _____ up the hill.**

_____

- -

6 **I _____ a big pig.**

Action Words

 An action word tells what happens.

Look at each picture. Read the words. Write the action word.

1   **I can see.**

_____
- - - - - - - - - - - - - - - - - - -
_____

2   **The cat sits.**

_____
- - - - - - - - - - - - - - - - - - -
_____

3   **Mom mops.**

_____
- - - - - - - - - - - - - - - - - - -
_____

4   **We run fast.**

_____
- - - - - - - - - - - - - - - - - - -
_____

5   **It hops a lot.**

_____
- - - - - - - - - - - - - - - - - - -
_____

Action Words

Read each sentence.
Fill in the circle next to the action word.

1 I sit on a hill.

ⓐ I ⓑ sit ⓒ hill

2 The rat ran fast.

ⓐ ran ⓑ rat ⓒ fast

3 We mop a lot.

ⓐ We ⓑ lot ⓒ mop

4 The dog digs up sand.

ⓐ dog ⓑ sand ⓒ digs

5 Pam hops up and down.

ⓐ hops ⓑ up ⓒ Pam

Describing Words

A describing word tells more about a person, place, or thing.

Read each sentence. Circle the word that tells about the cat.

1 I see a **big** cat.

2 The **fast** cat ran.

3 My cat is **bad**.

4 The **fat** cat naps.

Look at each cat. Circle the word that tells about it.

5 fat   little

6 big   little

Describing Words

 A describing word tells more about a person, place, or thing.

Look at each picture. Circle the words that tell about it.

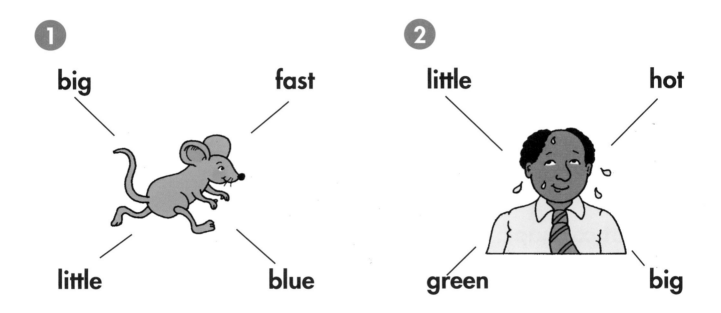

1

big   fast

little   blue

2

little   hot

green   big

Draw a line between each sentence and the picture that shows what it describes.

3 **It is fat.**

4 **They are little.**

Describing Words

Read each sentence. Fill in the circle next to the describing word.

1 **The silly cat can play.**

- ⬭ silly
- ⬭ cat
- ⬭ play

2 **The bad rat will run.**

- ⬭ bad
- ⬭ run
- ⬭ rat

3 **The black dog naps.**

- ⬭ dog
- ⬭ black
- ⬭ naps

4 **The cow is big.**

- ⬭ cow
- ⬭ is
- ⬭ big

5 **A green frog can hop.**

- ⬭ frog
- ⬭ green
- ⬭ hop

Telling Sentences

 A telling sentence tells something.

Circle the capital letter at the beginning of each telling sentence. Then circle the period at the end of each telling sentence.

1 I see the basket.

2 The cat is in the basket.

3 Hats can go in it.

4 The sock can go in it.

Draw a line under each telling sentence.

5 I can fill the basket.

6 Can you get the mop?

7 We can clean.

Telling Sentences

 A telling sentence tells something.

Draw a line to match each sentence with the picture that shows what the sentence tells.

1 She has a mop.

2 The dog is on top.

3 Dan gets the hats.

4 Ron can clean spots.

Read the sentences. Circle the capital letter and period in the telling sentence.

5 Put it in the pot.   **6** Is it in the pan?

Telling Sentences

Read the sentences. Fill in the circle next to each sentence that tells something.

1

◯ Can you get the basket?

◯ You can get it.

◯ Can you fill it?

2

◯ The basket is big.

◯ Is the basket big?

◯ Why is it big?

3

◯ What can go in it?

◯ Will the hat go in?

◯ The hat is in the basket.

4

◯ A cat can not go in it.

◯ Can a cat go in?

◯ Will a cat go in it?

5

◯ Can we fill it?

◯ We can fill the basket.

◯ Will you fill it?

Exclamation Sentences

 Exclamatory sentences show strong feelings such as excitement, surprise, or fear. They end with exclamation marks. (!)

Read each sentence. Circle each exclamation mark. Draw a line under the capital letter at the beginning of each sentence.

1 **Help! The rat is on top!**

2 **Get the cat!**

3 **This cat is bad!**

4 **Uh-oh! The cat is wet!**

Read each set of sentences. Draw a line under the sentence or sentences that show strong feeling.

5 **Oh my! Get the dog!**

Let's get the dog.

6 **The dog runs.**

Oh! The dog runs!

Exclamation Sentences

Choose the sentence in each pair that shows strong feeling. Write it on the line. Put an exclamation mark at the end.

> Exclamatory sentences show strong feeling, such as excitement, surprise, or fear. They end with an exclamation mark. (!)

1   Run to the show   We will go to the show

_____

2   I'm late for it   Oh my, I'm very late

_____

3   What a great show   I liked the show

_____

4   The floor is wet   Watch out, the floor is wet

_____

5   We had fun   Wow, we had lots of fun

_____

Exclamation Sentences

Read each group of sentences. Fill in the circle next to the sentence or sentences that show strong feeling.

1

○ The cow is on the hill.

○ The cow likes grass.

○ Yes! The cow can kick!

2

○ That cat is bad!

○ That cat naps.

○ Is the cat on the mat?

3

○ The rat will run.

○ That rat runs fast!

○ The rat can hop.

4

○ Oh no! A frog is in my house!

○ A frog hops.

○ The frog is green.

5

○ The pot can get hot.

○ The pot is hot!

○ Fill the pot with mud.

Singular/Plural Nouns

 Many nouns, or naming words, add -s to show more than one.

Read each sentence. Draw a line under each naming word that means more than one.

1 **I see hats and a cap.**   **2** **It sits on eggs.**

3 **The girls swim.**   **4** **Pam can pet cats.**

Read each sentence. Write the naming word that means more than one.

_____

----

5 **The mugs are hot.**   _____

_____

----

6 **Mud is on my hands.**   _____

Singular/Plural Nouns

 Many nouns, or naming words, add -s to show more than one.

Read the sets of sentences. Draw a line under the sentence that has a naming word that names more than one.

1 Jan has her mittens.

Jan has her mitten.

2 She will run up a hill.

She will run up hills.

3 Jan runs with her dogs.

Jan runs with her dog.

4 The dogs can jump.

The dog can jump.

Look at each picture. Read each word. Write the plural naming word that matches the picture.

5

cat _____

6

sock _____

Singular/Plural Nouns

Read each sentence. Fill in the circle next to the naming word that means more than one.

1 Jim gets mud on his hands.

⭕ gets

⭕ hands

⭕ mud

2 Pam can fill the pots with mud.

⭕ pots

⭕ mud

⭕ fill

3 The dogs dig fast.

⭕ dig

⭕ fast

⭕ dogs

4 The ants are on the plant.

⭕ ants

⭕ plant

⭕ are

5 The frogs hop.

⭕ The

⭕ frogs

⭕ hop

Action Words

An action word tells what happens.

Read each sentence. Circle the word that tells what happens.

1 **The hen sits.**

2 **Mom sees the hen.**

3 **The dog digs.**

4 **The cat naps.**

Read the words. Use the words to finish the sentences.

| sees | run |

5 **She** _____ **eggs.**

6 **It can** _____ **fast.**

Action Words

 An action word tells what happens.

| talk |
| play |
| dance |
| run |

Look at the pictures. Read the action words in the box.
Write the correct action word on the line.

1 Sue and Al ____play____ ball.

2 The bears _____ .

3 Rabbit and Pig _____ .

4 Tami and Lee _____ fast.

The words in the box tell what the characters in the pictures are doing.

Action Words

Read each sentence. Fill in the circle next to the action word.

1 **The hen sits.**
- ⬭ hen
- ⬭ sits
- ⬭ The

2 **The cat naps in the van.**
- ⬭ naps
- ⬭ cat
- ⬭ van

3 **The green frog hops.**
- ⬭ frog
- ⬭ green
- ⬭ hops

4 **The dog digs.**
- ⬭ digs
- ⬭ dog
- ⬭ The

5 **The big pig ran.**
- ⬭ big
- ⬭ pig
- ⬭ ran

Naming Words

 A naming word names a person, place, or thing.

Read each sentence. Draw a line under the naming word.

1 We play at school.

2 The ball is fast.

3 The girl kicks.

4 The friends run.

Look at each box. Circle the naming word that belongs in that box.

Person	Place	Thing
girl	ball	Pam
school	Bill	man
ball	school	ball

Naming Words

 *A naming word names a person, place, or thing.*

Read each sentence. Circle each naming word. Draw a line to match the sentence to the picture of the naming word.

1 **Run and kick in the park.**

2 **Kick with a foot.**

3 **Kick the ball.**

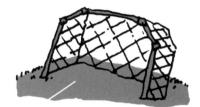

4 **The girl will run to get it.**

5 **Kick it to the net.**

Naming Words

Read each sentence. Fill in the circle next to the word that names a person, place, or thing.

1 Let's play in the park.

- ◯ play
- ◯ Let's
- ◯ park

2 The girl can run and kick.

- ◯ girl
- ◯ run
- ◯ kick

3 Kick the ball.

- ◯ ball
- ◯ the
- ◯ kick

4 The friend can jump.

- ◯ can
- ◯ jump
- ◯ friend

5 Jump to the net.

- ◯ get
- ◯ net
- ◯ jump

Word Order

Words in a sentence must be in an order that makes sense.

Read each group of words. Circle the words that are in an order that makes sense. Draw a line under each capital letter.

1 The king is sad.

sad. king is The

2 bake Let's cake. him a

Let's bake him a cake.

3 the king Tell to come.

Tell the king to come.

4 Let's eat the cake.

eat Let's the cake.

Read the words. Write them in order.

king The eats .

_____

- -

_____

Word Order

 *Words in a sentence must be in an order that makes sense.*

These words are mixed up. Put them in order.
Then write each sentence.

1 snow. bear likes This

_____

_____

2 water cold. The is

_____

_____

3 fast. The runs bear

_____

_____

4 play. bears Two

_____

_____

Word Order

Read each group of words. Then fill in the circle next to the words that are in an order that makes sense.

1

◯ **Pam will bake a cake.**

◯ **bake Pam a will cake.**

◯ **will Pam cake. a bake**

2

◯ **will king. the see Pam**

◯ **king. Pam see will the**

◯ **Pam will see the king.**

3

◯ **duck. The king has a**

◯ **The king has a duck.**

◯ **has a king The duck.**

4

◯ **lake. the in is The duck**

◯ **The duck is in the lake.**

◯ **The lake. duck in is the**

5

◯ **The king will eat cake.**

◯ **king will The cake. eat**

◯ **cake. king will The eat**

Capitalizing Titles

 Important words in a title are capitalized.

Circle all the words that are capitalized.

What to See at Night

The Light of the Moon

★ See Many Stars! ★

The Sun and the Moon

Now use some of the words from the titles above to write your own titles.

_____

- -

_____

_____

- -

_____

Capitalizing Titles

Important words in a title are capitalized.

Read the titles. Circle all the words that should be capitalized.

1 look at the stars!

2 the moon shines at night

3 we see planets

4 many moons shine

5 night and day

Read each set of titles. Draw a line under the correct title.

6 The Sun in the Sky

the sun in the sky

7 See the stars!

See the Stars!

Capitalizing Titles

Read the titles. Fill in the circle next to the title with the correct words capitalized.

1
- ◯ Where Is the Sun?
- ◯ Where is the sun?
- ◯ Where Is The Sun?

2
- ◯ many cats to see
- ◯ Many cats To See
- ◯ Many Cats to See

3
- ◯ Day and Night
- ◯ day And night
- ◯ Day And Night

4
- ◯ how many pigs?
- ◯ How Many Pigs?
- ◯ How many pigs?

5
- ◯ the Big Bad wolf
- ◯ the big, bad wolf
- ◯ The Big, Bad Wolf

Naming Words

 A naming word names a person, place, or thing.

Read each sentence. Draw a line under the word or words that name the person, place, or thing in each sentence.

1 **The pot is big.**   **2** **The pan is big.**

3 **See the top?**   **4** **Jim can mop.**

Draw a line from each sentence to the picture that shows the naming word in that sentence.

5 **The pot is hot.**

6 **See the pan?**

7 **Jim is fast.**

Naming Words

A naming word names a person, place, or thing.

Circle the naming words in the sentences.

1 **Jan can go in a van.**

2 **The van can go fast.**

3 **The van is on a hill.**

4 **Dan sees Jan.**

Draw a picture of a person, place, or thing.
Write a sentence about your picture.
Circle the naming word.

5 _____

Naming Words

Read each sentence. Fill in the circle next to the naming word.

1 **See the hot pans?**

- ⬯ **hot**
- ⬯ **See**
- ⬯ **pans**

2 **See Jim mop fast.**

- ⬯ **fast**
- ⬯ **Jim**
- ⬯ **See**

3 **The cat naps.**

- ⬯ **cat**
- ⬯ **The**
- ⬯ **naps**

4 **The rat hid.**

- ⬯ **The**
- ⬯ **rat**
- ⬯ **hid**

5 **Can the cat see?**

- ⬯ **see**
- ⬯ **cat**
- ⬯ **Can**

Linking Verbs

Is, are, was, and *were* are linking verbs. *Is* tells about one. *Are* tells about more than one. *Was* tells about one in the past. *Were* tells about more than one in the past.

Read each sentence. Draw a line under the linking verb is, are, was, or were.

1 **The hen is digging.**

2 **The chicks were helping.**

3 **The pig was having fun.**

4 **The cat and duck are playing.**

Read each sentence. Circle now or in the past to show when it happens or happened.

5 **The hen is planting.**   now   in the past

6 **The cat was not helping.**   now   in the past

7 **The chicks are with the hen.**   now   in the past

Linking Verbs

 Is, are, was, and were are linking verbs. Is tells about one. Are tells about more than one. Was tells about one in the past. Were tells about more than one in the past.

Circle the linking verb. Write now or past to tell when the action happens or happened.

1 The chicks are eating.   _____

2 The duck is swimming.   _____

3 The cat was napping.   _____

4 The pig is digging.   _____

5 They were playing.   _____

Linking Verbs

Fill in the circle next to the linking verb that completes each sentence.

1 The hen ___ sitting.

○ was

○ are

○ were

2 They ___ playing.

○ were

○ is

○ was

3 The pigs ___ digging.

○ was

○ is

○ are

4 The duck ___ swimming.

○ were

○ is

○ are

5 The chicks ___ napping.

○ was

○ is

○ are

Capitalizing Names and First Words

The first word in a sentence starts with a capital letter. Sometimes words that name a person, place, or thing begin with a capital letter.

Read the sentences. Circle the words that are capitalized.

1 The goats Gruff have a problem.

2 They do not like the Troll.

3 His name is Nosey.

4 He is big and bad.

Draw a line to match each sentence to why the underlined word is capitalized.

5 Dan and <u>Pam</u> like the play.

First word in a sentence.

6 <u>They</u> will read it Jim.

Names a person, place, to or thing.

Capitalizing Names

 Sometimes the names of people, places, and things are special.
They begin with a capital letter.

Circle the special names in the picture. Write each one correctly on a line.

1 _____

2 _____

3 _____

4 _____

Capitalizing Names and First Words

Read each sentence. Fill in the circle next to the word that needs a capital letter.

1 i like the goats Gruff.

- ⬭ Goats
- ⬭ The
- ⬭ I

2 I read the story with ron.

- ⬭ Read
- ⬭ Story
- ⬭ Ron

3 Little gruff had a problem.

- ⬭ Had
- ⬭ Gruff
- ⬭ Problem

4 troll was on the bridge.

- ⬭ A
- ⬭ Bridge
- ⬭ Troll

5 His name was nosey.

- ⬭ Name
- ⬭ Nosey
- ⬭ His

Holiday Photos

The naming part of a sentence can be a person, a place, or a thing.

Use your own naming parts to write a complete sentence about each picture.

_____

- -

_____

- -

_____

_____

- -

_____

- -

_____

More Holiday Photos

Use your own naming parts to write a complete sentence .

_____

_____

_____

_____

_____

_____

_____

_____

 Look at your family's holiday pictures. On another piece of paper, write a sentence telling about two of them.

Name _____

No Bones About It!

*A sentence has an **action part**. It tells what is happening.*

Colour the bone that tells the action part in each sentence below.

1. 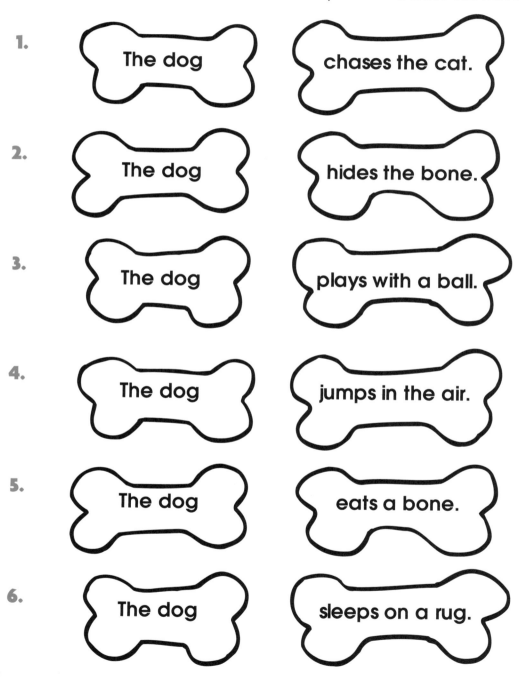 The dog   chases the cat.

2. The dog   hides the bone.

3. The dog   plays with a ball.

4. The dog   jumps in the air.

5. The dog   eats a bone.

6. The dog   sleeps on a rug.

 On another piece of paper, rewrite your favourite sentence.

Mighty Good Sentences

Choose the ending that tells what each dog is doing. Remember to use periods.

is eating.

is sleeping.

is jumping.

is barking.

1. The white dog _____

2. The grey dog _____

3. The spotted dog _____

4. The striped dog _____

 On another piece of paper, draw another dog and write a sentence about it.

A Busy Classroom

*The action part of a sentence is called the **verb**.*

Complete each sentence with an action verb to tell what is happening in the picture. Remember to use periods.

1. Mr. Downs _____

_____

2. The fish _____

_____

3. James _____

_____

4. Cara _____

On another piece of paper, write a sentence about your teacher. Circle the action word.

Pencil It In

Sometimes the verb does not show action.
It still tells what is happening.

For example: I know the answer.

I am hungry.

Choose a verb from the Word Bank
to complete each sentence.

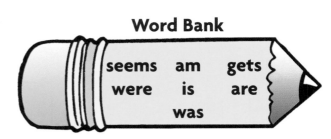

Word Bank

seems   am   gets
were   is   are
was

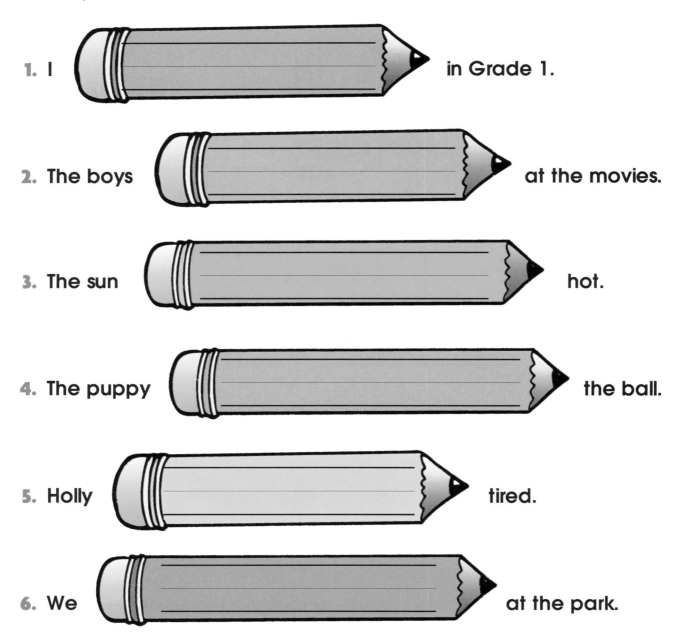

1. I _____ in Grade 1.

2. The boys _____ at the movies.

3. The sun _____ hot.

4. The puppy _____ the ball.

5. Holly _____ tired.

6. We _____ at the park.

Topsy-Turvy!

 A sentence has a verb that tells what is happening.

Write five silly sentences that tell what is happening in the pictures.

1. _____

_____

2. _____

_____

3. _____

_____

4. _____

_____

5. _____

What Is Going On?

Look around you. Write four sentences that tell what is happening.

1. _____

2. _____

3. _____

4. _____

 Find five action words in your favourite book. Write them on another piece of paper.

The Caboose

 *A sentence is more interesting when it tells **where** the action is happening.*

In each caboose, draw a picture to show where each sentence takes place.

1.

The plane flew into the clouds.

2.

The princess played in the castle.

3.

The boys fished in the lake.

Chugging Along

Write an ending for each sentence that tells where the action takes place.

naming part　　the action　　where

1. The monkey　swings　_____

2. The ball　flew　_____

3. Jenna's family　went　_____

4. The pig　slept　_____

5. The glass　fell　_____

When Was That?

*A sentence may also tell **when** the action takes place.*

Circle the part that tells when in each sentence.

1. Sir John A. Macdonald lived long ago.

2. The mail carrier was late yesterday.

3. The bear slept in winter.

4. We are going to the zoo today.

5. The leaves change in the fall.

6. I lost my tooth last night.

7. It rained all day.

8. The party starts at noon.

9. We got home yesterday.

10. We ate turkey on Thanksgiving Day.

11. The kitten was playing this morning.

12. Tomorrow I am going to my grandmother's house.

 On another piece of paper, make a time line of your life. Use it to write two sentences that tell when.

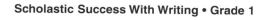

My Busy Day

 Part of a sentence may tell **when** *the action happened.*

Write the beginning part of each sentence to tell about your day.
Draw a picture to match each sentence.

_____

_____

_____

_____ this morning.

_____

_____

_____

_____ this afternoon.

_____

_____

_____

_____ tonight.

 On another piece of paper, write four sentences and draw four pictures to tell about your best day ever.

Silly Sentences

A sentence may have three parts: a naming part, an action, and a part that tells where or when.

Complete each missing part to make silly sentences.

	the naming part	the action	where or when
1.	The monkey		on his head.
2.	My dad	is hopping	
3.		flipped	in the forest.
4.	The ball	bounced	
5.	My shoes		at the pool.
6.	The snake	twisted	
7.	The bubbles	filled	

On another piece of paper, write a new sentence by scrambling three parts listed above. For example, use the naming part from #1, the action part from #2, and where or when from #3. Draw a picture of your sentence.

Sweet Sentences

Use choices from each part to make three "sweet" sentences.

naming part	action	where or when
I	ate doughnuts	at the bakery
She	ate candy	at the party
He	chewed gum	at the circus

 On another piece of paper, name the three parts of this sentence: The doughnut shop closed at noon.

Home Sweet Home

Write three sentences about the picture. For example: The dog is sleeping outside.

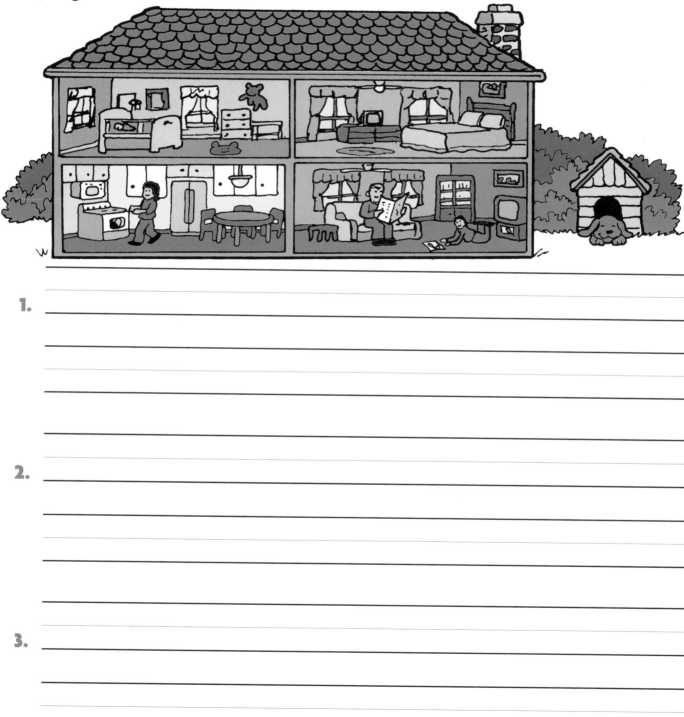

1. _____

_____

_____

2. _____

_____

_____

3. _____

_____

_____

The Construction Crew

Write three sentences about the picture. Include three parts in each sentence.

1. _____
   _____
   _____
   _____

2. _____
   _____
   _____
   _____

3. _____
   _____
   _____
   _____

Mystery Boxes

Describing words help you imagine how something looks, feels, smells, sounds, or tastes.

Read the describing words to guess the mystery object. Use the Word Bank to help you.

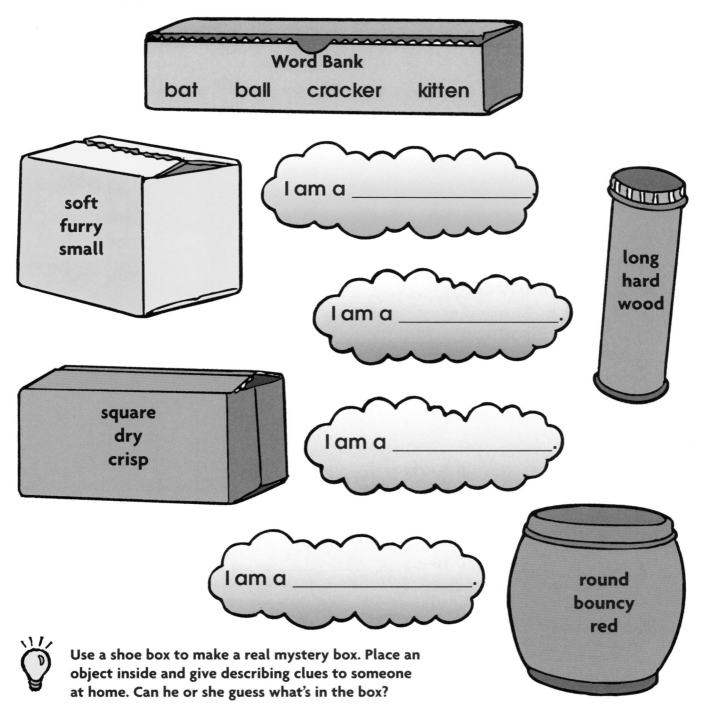

Word Bank

bat   ball   cracker   kitten

soft
furry
small

I am a _____

long
hard
wood

I am a _____.

square
dry
crisp

I am a _____.

I am a _____.

round
bouncy
red

Use a shoe box to make a real mystery box. Place an object inside and give describing clues to someone at home. Can he or she guess what's in the box?

Sensational Words

Choose words from the Word Bank to describe each picture.

It tastes _____.

It looks _____.

It feels _____.

Word Bank

bumpy

crunchy

furry

gray

red

salty

smooth

squeaky

sweet

It feels _____.

It tastes _____.

It sounds _____.

It looks _____.

It sounds _____.

It feels _____.

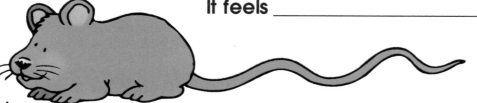

💡 **Find two objects outside. On another piece of paper, write two adjectives to describe each object.**

Pretty Packages

 The describing words in a sentence help the reader paint a picture in his or her mind.

Write three words to describe each gift. Then colour them to match.

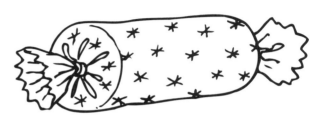

_____ (colour)

_____ (colour)

_____ (pattern)

_____ (colour)

_____ (colour)

_____ (pattern)

_____ (colour)

_____ (colour)

_____ (pattern)

_____ (colour)

_____ (colour)

_____ (pattern)

 Describe a "mystery object" to a friend. Can he or she guess what you are describing?

What's Inside?

Use the describing words from page 243 to write a sentence
about each package. For example: I found a swimsuit in the
yellow square box.

1. I found _____ in the

_____

_____ package.

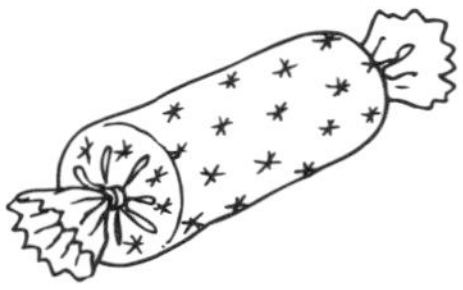

2. I found _____

_____ in the

_____

_____ package.

3. I found _____

_____ in the

_____

_____ package.

4. I found _____

_____

_____ in the

_____ package.

A Walk in the Park

Describing words make a sentence more interesting.

Write describing words to finish each sentence.

1. A _____ duck is

   swimming in the _____ pond.

2. A _____ man is walking

   his _____ dog.

3. A _____ girl is

   flying a _____ kite.

4. A _____ woman is sitting

   on a _____ .

 On another piece of paper, draw a picture of your favourite animal at the zoo. Then write two words to describe this animal.

Around Town

Write a sentence for each picture. Use the describing word in the sentence.

large

_____
_____
_____
_____

beautiful

_____
_____
_____
_____

crowded

_____
_____
_____
_____

noisy

_____
_____
_____
_____

 On another piece of paper, write five words that describe your street.

Name _____

Keep It in Order

 Sentences can be written in order to tell a story.

Finish each story by writing sentences about the last pictures.

1. First, the spider crawls up.

Next, _____

_____

Last, _____

2. First, there is a tadpole.

Next, _____

_____

Last, _____

What's Next?

 Sentences can be written in order to give directions.

Finish each set of directions by writing sentences about the last pictures.

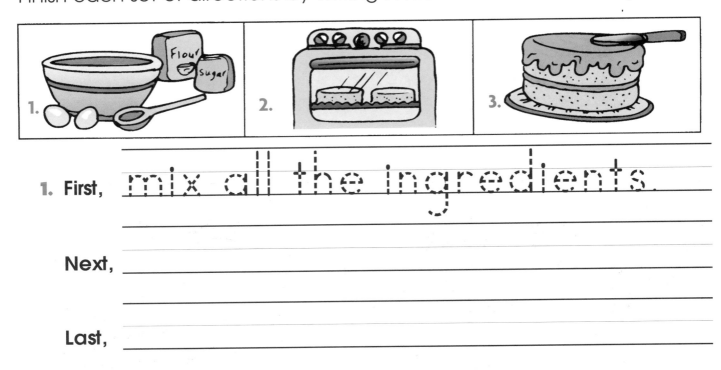

1. First, <u>mix all the ingredients.</u>

Next, _____

_____

Last, _____

2. First, <u>put your dog in the tub.</u>

Next, _____

_____

Last, _____

Which Title Fits?

*The name of a story is called the **title**. It matches with the story. Most of the words in a title begin with capital letters.*

Match each title with its story. Write the title above the picture.

A Big Beak	The Big Win
My Space Friend	A Knight's Tale

_____
(title)

_____
(title)

_____
(title)

_____
(title)

A Terrific Title

Fill in the missing words to make your own story. Then write a title that fits with your story. Draw a picture about your story in the box.

_____
(title)

One _____ day,

_____ took his pet

_____ for a walk. First,

they went to the _____.

Then they walked to _____'s

house. Last, they went home to _____

_____. It was a

_____ day!

Story Strips

 A story has a beginning, middle, and end.

Write a sentence to tell about each part of the story. Remember to give the story a title.

Beginning

_____
(title)

- -

Middle

- -

End

- -

More Story Strips

 A story has a beginning, middle, and end.

Think of a story you know well. Write about the beginning, middle, and end parts. Draw pictures to match. Be sure to give your story a title.

_____
(title)

Beginning

_____
- -
_____

Middle

_____
- -
_____

End

_____
- -

 Fold a piece of paper two times to make a storybook. Write a story and draw pictures to match. Do not forget to write a title for your story.

MAPS

Places in Pictures

Pretend you are on
a cloud in the sky.
You look down.
You take a photo.
Here it is!

Circle **YES** if you see the thing in the photo.
Circle **NO** if you do not.

1. house   YES   NO

2. street   YES   NO

3. tree   YES   NO

4. river   YES   NO

5. What else do you see? _____

You can show a place on a map.
A map is a drawing of a place from above.
This map shows the same place that the photo does.

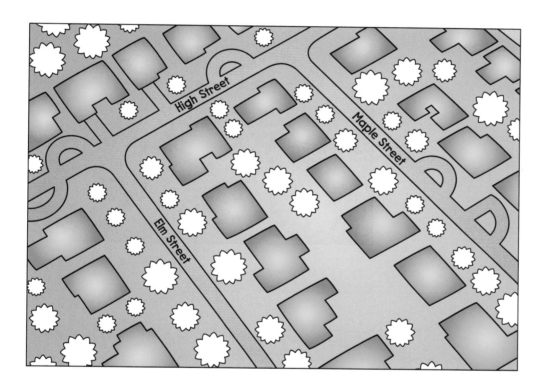

6. Find a street on the photo.
   Then find the same street on the map.
   Write the name of the street._____

7. The trees on the map are not coloured.
   Color them green.

8. Find a swimming pool in the photo.
   Draw it in the same place on the map.

Making a Map

This picture shows a toy store.

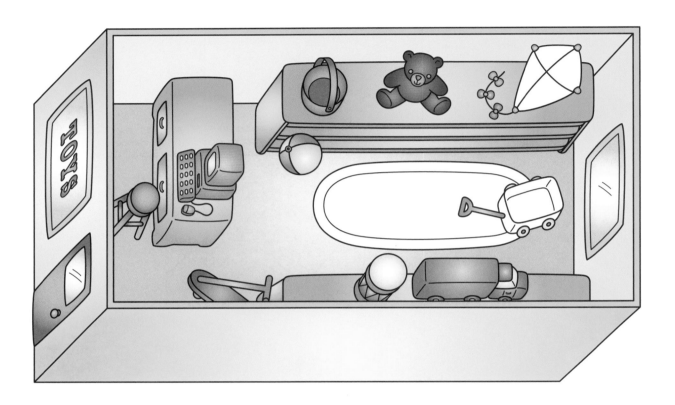

1. Colour the kite yellow.

2. Colour the rug green.

3. Colour the wagon red.

4. What is next to the drum? _____

5. Can you buy a teddy bear here? _____

This map shows the same toy store.
You can help draw the map.

6. **Find the ball in the picture.**
   Make it the same colour on the map.

7. **Find the stool in the picture.**
   Make it the same colour on the map.

8. **Find the rug in the picture.**
   Draw it on the map in the same place.

Map Words

Many map words tell where things are.

The bird is **near** the branch.

The bird is **far** from the branch.

The bird is to the **left** of the birdhouse.

The bird is to the **right** of the birdhouse.

The bird is **above** the bath.

The bird is **below** the bath.

Write a word to complete each sentence.

near   far   left   right   above

1. The bird is _____ from the birdhouse.

2. The girl is _____ the birdhouse.

3. The bird is _____ the grass.

4. The birdhouse is to the _____ of the girl.

5. The path is to the _____ of the girl.

Big and Small Spaces

Maps can show big spaces or small spaces.

Map 1: This map shows a school playground.

Map 2: This map shows all of the school grounds.

Circle **YES** if the sentence is true.
Circle **NO** if the sentence is not true.

1. **The school is bigger than the trees.**   YES NO

2. **The playground is bigger than the parking lot.** YES NO

3. **The school is to the right of the playground.**   YES NO

4. **The trees are to the right of the playground.**   YES NO

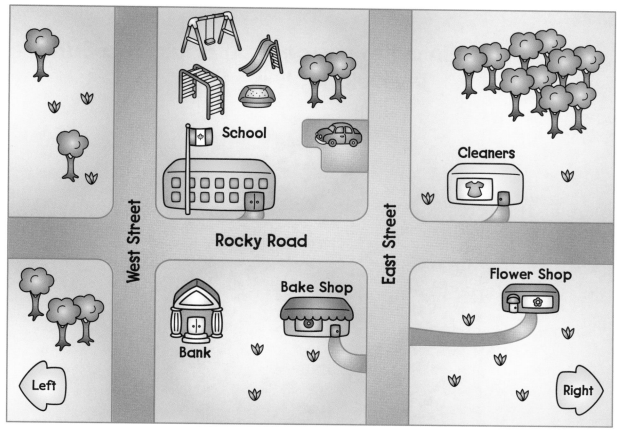

Map 3: This map shows three streets. Can you find the school?

5. **What is the biggest building on this map?** _____

6. **What is the smallest building on this map?** _____

7. **Look at all three maps. Which map shows the biggest space?** _____

8. **Which map shows the smallest space?** _____

Looking at Earth

If you were in outer space, you could see Earth. It would look like this.

1. **What shape is Earth?** _____

2. **Who lives on Earth?** _____

3. **Draw something that is the same shape as Earth.**

A Globe

A **globe** is a model of Earth.
It is the same shape as Earth.

1. What colours do you see on the globe?

_____

2. What colour stands for water?

_____

3. Is a globe smaller or bigger than Earth?

_____

Directions

Earth has four main directions.
They are north, south, east, and west.

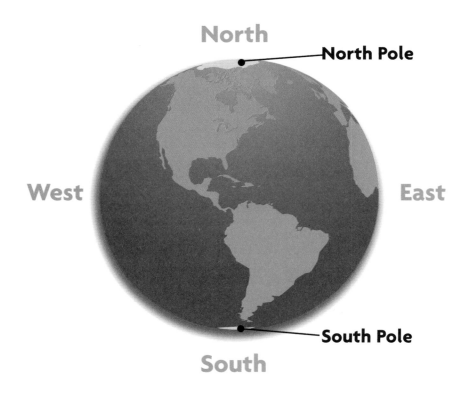

North is the direction toward the North Pole.
South is the direction toward the South Pole.

Can you find east and west on the picture, too?

1. What direction is the opposite of north? _____

2. What direction is the opposite of west? _____

Directions help you find places on a map.
This map shows a camp.
Point to the four directions.

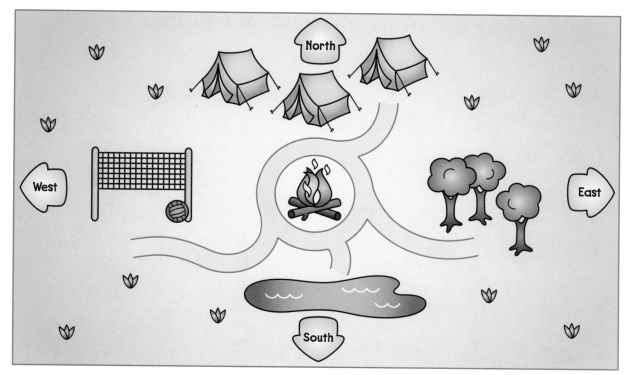

Where is each thing?
Write a direction word to describe it.

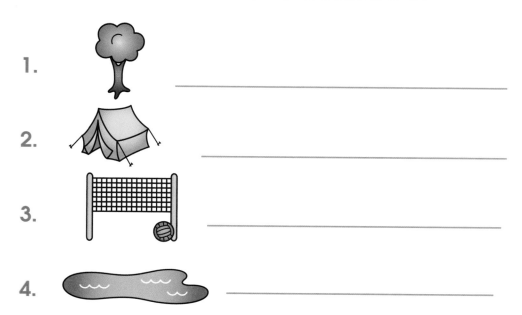

1. _____

2. _____

3. _____

4. _____

Using Directions

Directions tell you which way to go.
This map shows a pet shop.

Write the direction word that tells how to get there.

1. from 🐦 to 🐱 _____

2. from 🐟 to 🐭 _____

3. from 🐕 to 🏪 _____

4. from 🏪 to 🥫 _____

Come to the fair! You can have fun.

Draw a line to show where you go.

1. Start at the gate. Go north to the . Mmmm!

2. Now go west. Stop and ride on the .

3. Walk to the east. Get your face painted like a .

4. From here, go west and
   then north. Stop and play at the .

5. In which direction is the gate from the ?

Symbols

A symbol is a drawing that stands for something real.

The photo shows a road.

This is a symbol for a road.

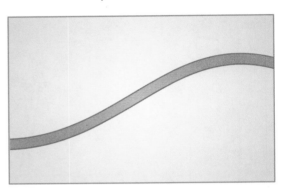

Draw a line to match each photo to the correct symbol.

1.

2.

3.

4.

a.

b.

c.

d.

Here are some more symbols.

Draw the correct symbol next to each photo.

1.

3.

2.

4.

Symbols on Maps

Most maps have symbols.
A map key tells what each symbol stands for.

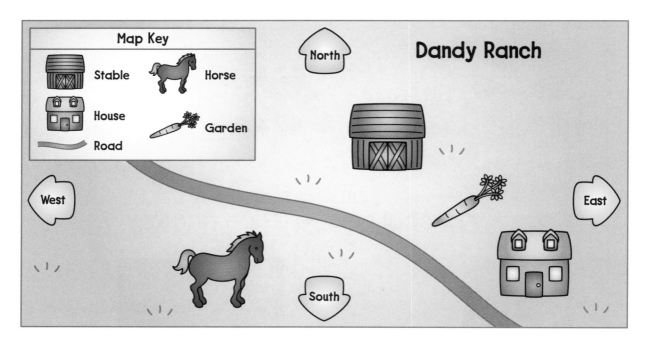

Use the map key.
Write what each symbol stands for.

1.  _____

2.  _____

3.  _____

4.  _____

The ranch has one new animal.

Circle the new animal on the map.
Use the map key to answer the questions.

1. Is the horse north or south of the road? _____

2. What does mean? _____

3. Is the garden east or west of the house? _____

4. Find the forest on the map.
   Add a tree symbol to the map key.

Land and Water

Earth has different kinds of land.

Some land is flat.
A **plain** is flat land.

Some land is very high. A
mountain is very high land.

Some land is higher than
a plain but not as high as
a mountain. This land is
called a **hill**.

1. **What is the highest kind of land?**

_____

2. **What is the flattest land?**

_____

3. **Which is higher, a hill or a plain?**

_____

Earth has lots of water.

Some water runs across the land. This water is called a **river.**

Some water has land all around it. This water is called a **lake**.

These symbols stand for different kinds of land and water. Write a word to tell what each symbol stands for.

4.  _____

6.  _____

5. _____

7. _____

A Land and Water Map

This picture shows different kinds of land and water.

1. **Find the river. Colour it blue.**

2. **Find a body of water with land all around it.**
   Write "lake" on it.

3. **Find the hills. Colour them light green.**

4. **Find the flat land. Write "plain" on it.**

This map shows land and water, too.

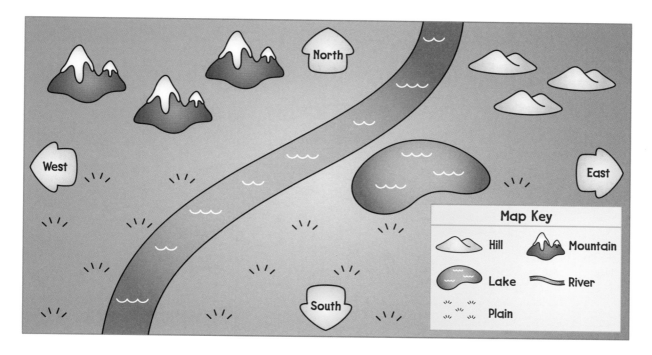

1. What does [image] mean? _____

2. Is the lake to the east or west of the river? _____

3. Are the mountains to the
   east or west of the hills? _____

4. Write a place where you can do each thing.

   climb _____   run _____

   swim _____   fish _____

A Park Map

This map shows a big park.
A park can have different kinds of land and water.

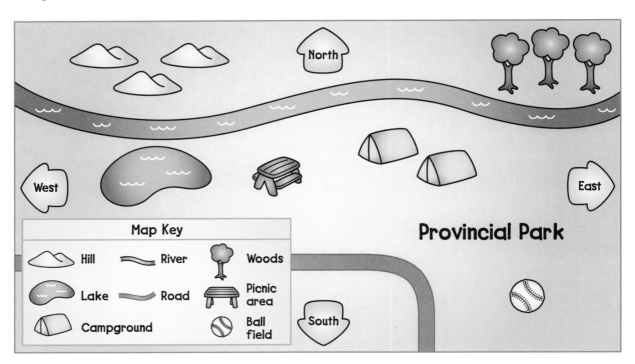

1. What does this symbol  mean? _____

2. Where can you sleep in this park? _____

3. What symbol shows where
   you can have a picnic? _____

4. Where can you ride a raft in this park? _____

5. Is the road to the east
   or west of the ball field? _____

This map shows a city park.

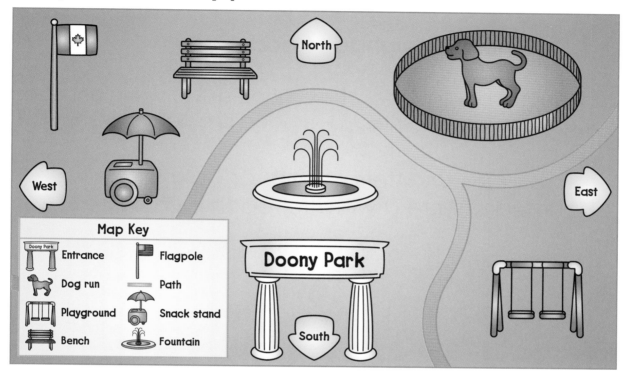

1. What is the name of this park?

   _____

2. Where can you get something to eat?

   _____

3. What is north of the entrance?

   _____

4. Where can your dog
   play in this park?

   _____

5. Where can you ride a swing?

   _____

6. In which direction
   would you walk from the  to the ?

   _____

A Neighbourhood Map

A map can show a neighbourhood.

A neighbourhood is a place where people live, work, and play. The people who live in a neighbourhood are neighbours.

These pictures show different parts of Dale's neighbourhood. Write a word for each picture.

1. 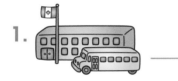 _____

2. _____

3. _____

4. _____

5. **Draw a picture of something in your neighbourhood.**

This map shows the neighbourhood where Dale lives.

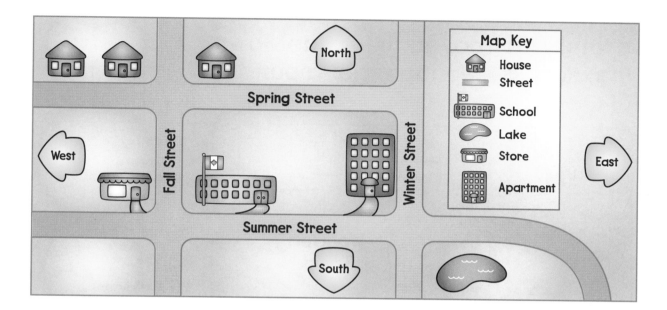

1. What does the symbol

 stand for? _____

2. Find the symbol for house.
   On what street are the houses? _____

3. Dale lives in an apartment.
   On what street does Dale live? _____

4. Dale is going to the store
   with her father. In which direction
   is the store from her home? _____

Going Places

Hari's family just moved to Wonder Town.
Use this map to help them get around.

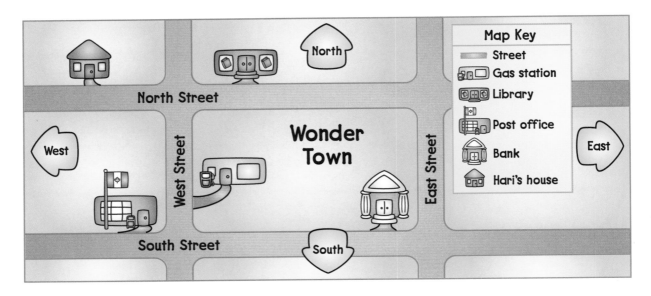

Tell Hari's family the street for each place.

1. **Hari's mother is going
   to the bank. It is on** _____.

2. **Hari's father is going
   to the gas station. It is on** _____.

3. **Hari's big brother is going
   to the library. It is on** _____.

4. **Hari's grandma is going
   to the post office. It is on** _____.

Hari goes to school the same way each day. He follows a route. A route is a way to go from one place to another.

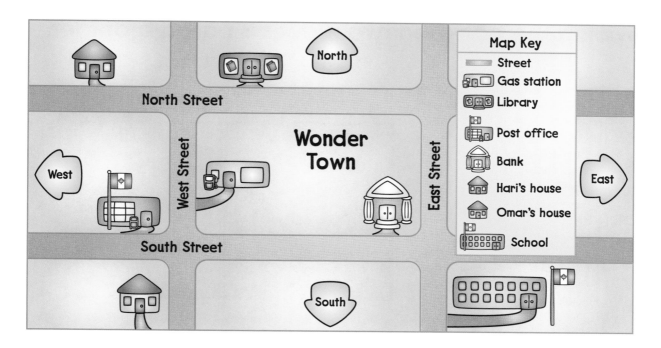

1. **Start at Hari's house.**
   Draw a line to show the route he can take to school.

2. **On what street is the school?** _____

3. **Omar is Hari's new friend.**
   Draw a line to show Omar's route to school.

4. **Does Omar live east or**
   west of the school? _____

5. **Is the library north or**
   south of the gas station? _____

Borders

Maps show where places begin and end.
A dividing line between two places is called a border.

Look at the fence in this photo. The fence shows where the border is.

Look at the line with dashes on this map. This line is a symbol. It stands for a border.

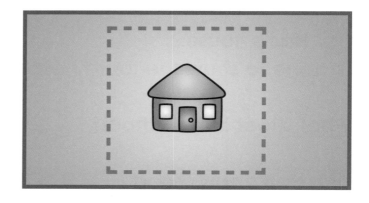

Maps show other kinds of borders, too. A river can be a border. So can a road. Draw an X on three kinds of borders on this map.

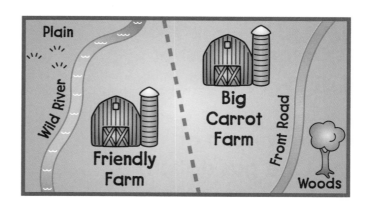

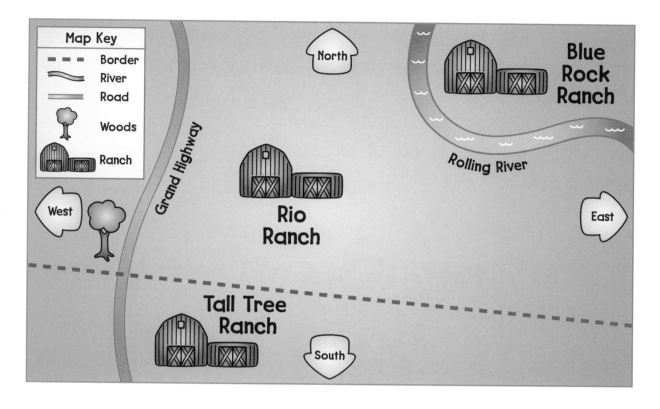

This map shows different borders.

1. This symbol ----- stands for a _____.

2. The border to the west of
   Rio Ranch is a _____.

3. What is the border between
   Rio Ranch and Blue Rock Ranch? _____

4. In which direction is Tall Tree Ranch
   from Rio Ranch? _____

5. Are the woods east or
   west of Rio Ranch? _____

North America

This map shows North America. North America is a **continent**.

A continent is a large body of land.
Canada is in North America.

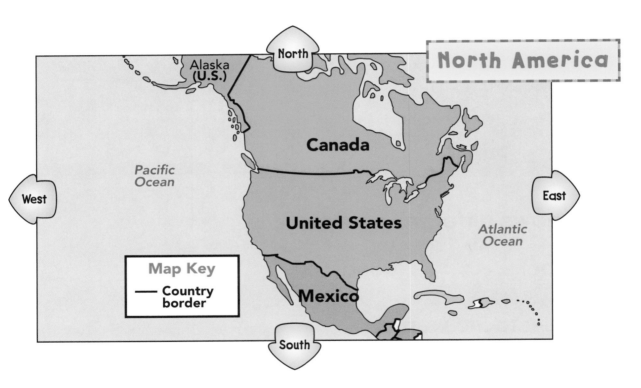

1. What does the symbol _____ mean? _____

2. Canada is a country. What country is next to it?

_____

3. In which direction is Mexico
   from the United States? _____

Around the continents are Earth's oceans.
An ocean is a very big body of salt water.

Earth has four oceans.
This map shows two of them.

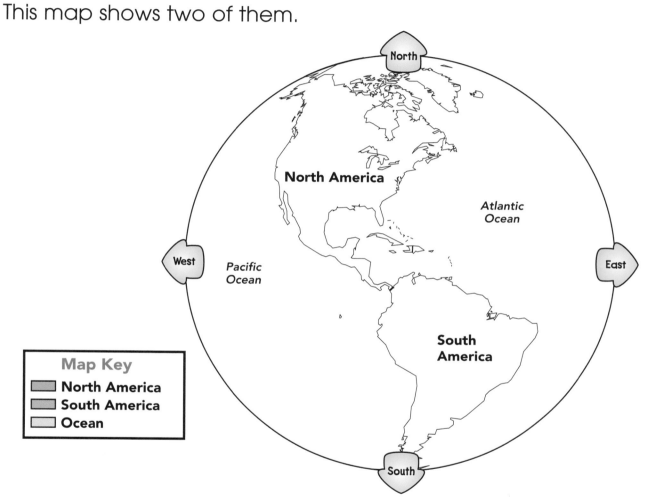

1. What ocean is to the
   east of North America? _____

2. What ocean is to the
   west of North America? _____

3. Colour the map to match the map key.

A World Map

Remember, Earth
is round like a ball. But
you can only see one
side of a ball at once.

1. Here is a map of Earth. It shows all of Earth's continents.
   Count to find seven continents.

2. The map shows the five oceans of
   Earth, too. What are their names?

   _____   _____

   _____   _____

   _____

3. What continent is north of Africa?_____

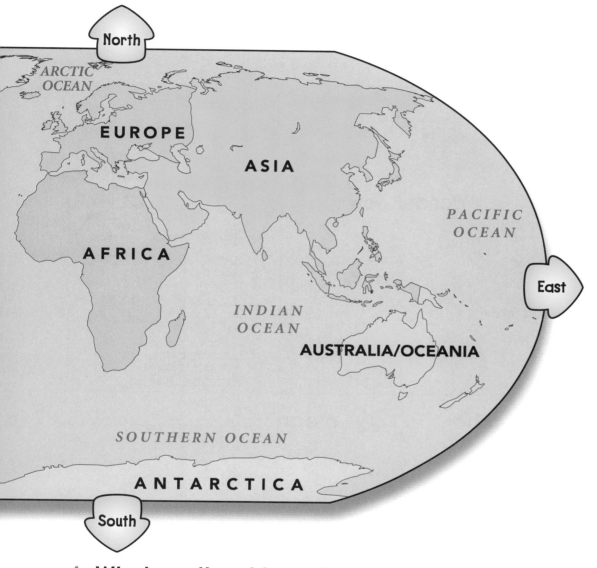

4. What continent is south of North America? _____

5. What ocean is west of Australia/Oceania? _____

6. What ocean is in the north part of Earth? _____

7. What continent is in the far south part of Earth? _____

Map Review

Use the map to answer the questions.

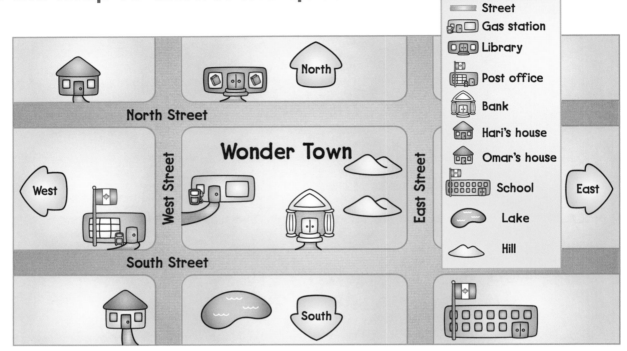

1. What does this symbol mean? _____

2. What kind of land is to
   the east of the bank? _____

3. On what street does Hari live? _____

4. Draw a route from Hari's house to Omar's house.

5. Where can Hari mail a letter? _____

6. Is Hari's house north or
   south of the school? _____

Thinking About Maps

You have learned a lot about maps. Use what you know to fill in the blanks.

1. The direction that is opposite of north

   — — — —

2. A body of water with land all around it

   — — — —

3. A dividing line between two places

   — — — — — —

4. A drawing that stands for something real

   — — — — —

5. Very high land

   — — — — — — —

6. A way to go from one place to another

   — — — —

7. A very big body of salt water

   — — — — —

Glossary

border	A border is a dividing line between two places.
continent	A continent is a large body of land. North America is a continent.
country	A country is a land and the people who live there.
direction	A direction tells where something is. The four main directions are north, south, east, and west.
east	East is one of the four main directions. East is the opposite of west.
Earth	Earth is the planet on which people live.
far	Far is a word that tells where things are. Far is the opposite of near.
globe	A globe is a model of Earth.
hill	A hill is land that is higher than a plain but not as high as a mountain.
lake	A lake is a body of water that has land all around it.
left	Left is a word that tells where things are. Left is the opposite of right.
map	A map is a drawing of a place from above. A map shows part or all of Earth.

map key	A map key is a list of symbols used on a map. The map key tells what each symbol means.
mountain	A mountain is very high land.
near	Near is a word that tells where things are. Near is the opposite of far.
neighbourhood	A neighbourhood is a place where people live and work.
north	North is one of the four main directions. North is the direction toward the North Pole.
ocean	An ocean is a very large body of water. Earth has five oceans.
plain	A plain is flat land.
right	Right is a word that tells where things are. Right is the opposite of left.
river	A river is a body of water that flows across the land.
route	A route is a way to go from one place to another.
south	South is one of the four main directions. South is the direction toward the South Pole.
symbol	A symbol is a drawing that stands for something real.
west	West is one of the four main directions. West is the opposite of east.

ADDITION & SUBTRACTION

Clowning Around

Add. Colour the picture
using the colour code.

Colour Code

1	pink
2	white
3	black
4	brown
5	purple
6	green
7	blue
8	orange
9	yellow
10	red

$5 + 2 =$

$6 + 3 =$

$\begin{array}{r} 4 \\ + 5 \\ \hline \end{array}$
$\begin{array}{r} 5 \\ + 0 \\ \hline \end{array}$

$\begin{array}{r} 2 \\ + 3 \\ \hline \end{array}$

$\begin{array}{r} 7 \\ + 2 \\ \hline \end{array}$
$\begin{array}{r} 4 \\ + 4 \\ \hline \end{array}$

$2 + 5 =$

$3 + 2 =$

$\begin{array}{r} 4 \\ + 3 \\ \hline \end{array}$

$\begin{array}{r} 3 \\ + 3 \\ \hline \end{array}$
$\begin{array}{r} 1 \\ + 0 \\ \hline \end{array}$
$\begin{array}{r} 4 \\ + 2 \\ \hline \end{array}$
$\begin{array}{r} 0 \\ + 1 \\ \hline \end{array}$
$\begin{array}{r} 5 \\ + 1 \\ \hline \end{array}$

$4 + 1 =$

$\begin{array}{r} 6 \\ + 2 \\ \hline \end{array}$

$\begin{array}{r} 2 \\ + 1 \\ \hline \end{array}$

$7 + 0 =$

$\begin{array}{r} 3 \\ + 0 \\ \hline \end{array}$

$\begin{array}{r} 3 \\ + 5 \\ \hline \end{array}$

$5 + 5 =$

$6 + 1 =$

$\begin{array}{r} 1 \\ + 1 \\ \hline \end{array}$

$7 + 3 =$

$3 + 1 =$

Name_____

Lovely Ladybugs

Write a number sentence to show how many spots each ladybug has.

$1 + 2 = 3$

___ + ___ = ___

___ + ___ = ___

___ + ___ = ___

___ + ___ = ___

___ + ___ = ___

___ + ___ = ___

___ + ___ = ___

___ + ___ = ___

 Colour the ladybug with the greatest number of spots red.
Colour the ladybug with the least number of spots blue.

Beautiful Bouquets

Look at the number on each bow. Draw more flowers to match the number written on the bow.

 Colour the bows with an even number yellow.
Colour the bows with an odd number purple.

Telephone Math

What kind of phone never rings? _____

To find out, solve the addition problems. Then use the code on the telephone to replace your answers with letters. The first one has been done for you.

$$\begin{array}{r} 6 \\ + 2 \\ \hline 8 \end{array}$$ __A__

$$\begin{array}{r} 5 \\ + 1 \\ \hline \end{array}$$ _____

$$\begin{array}{r} 4 \\ + 4 \\ \hline \end{array}$$ _____

$$\begin{array}{r} 3 \\ + 6 \\ \hline \end{array}$$ _____

$$\begin{array}{r} 3 \\ + 0 \\ \hline \end{array}$$ _____

$$\begin{array}{r} 3 \\ + 4 \\ \hline \end{array}$$ _____

$$\begin{array}{r} 2 \\ + 2 \\ \hline \end{array}$$ _____

$$\begin{array}{r} 2 \\ + 1 \\ \hline \end{array}$$ _____

$$\begin{array}{r} 1 \\ + 1 \\ \hline \end{array}$$ _____

$$\begin{array}{r} 0 \\ + 1 \\ \hline \end{array}$$ _____

 Write your telephone number in letters using the phone code above.

_____

High Flyer

Do the subtraction problems.

> If the answer is 1 or 2, colour the shape red.
>
> If the answer is 3 or 4, colour the shape blue.
>
> If the answer is 5 or 6, colour the shape yellow.
>
> If the answer is 7 or 8, colour the shape green.
>
> If the answer is 9, colour the shape black.
>
> Colour the other shapes the colours of your choice.

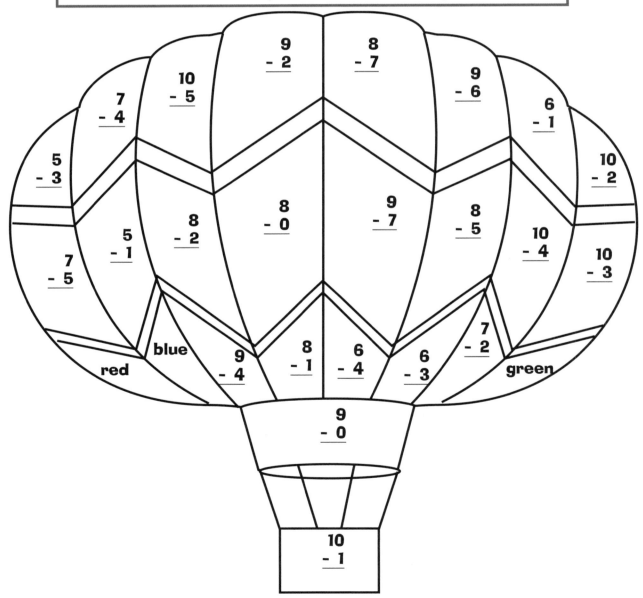

Name ______________________

Juggling Act

Cross out. Write how many are left.

4 – 2 = ____

3 – 1 = 2

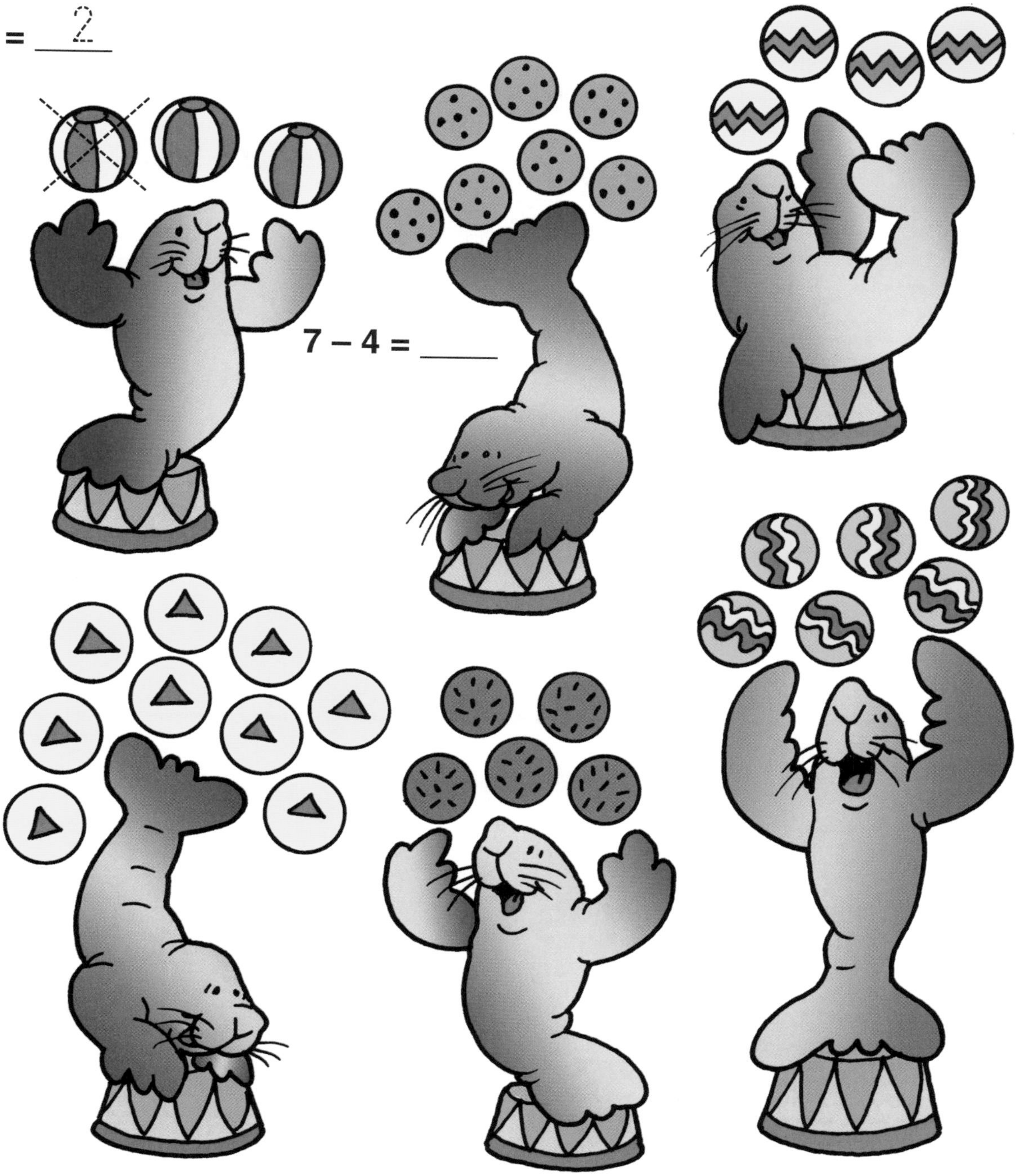

7 – 4 = ____

9 – 6 = ____

5 – 3 = ____

6 – 5 = ____

Ocean Life

Use the math picture on page 301 to count and write the number in each box. Subtract the numbers.

1.  ☐
   ☐
   –
   _____
   ☐

2.  ☐
   ☐
   –
   _____
   ☐

3.  ☐
   ☐
   –
   _____
   ☐

4.  ☐
   ☐
   –
   _____
   ☐

5. 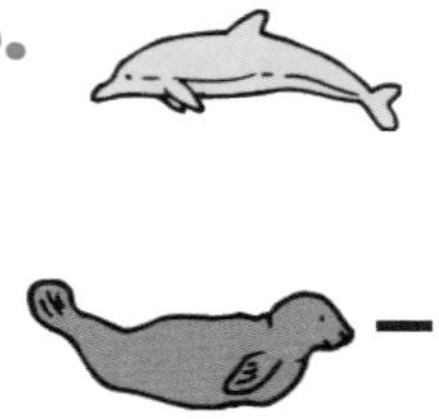 ☐
   ☐
   –
   _____
   ☐

6.  ☐
   ☐
   –
   _____
   ☐

7. 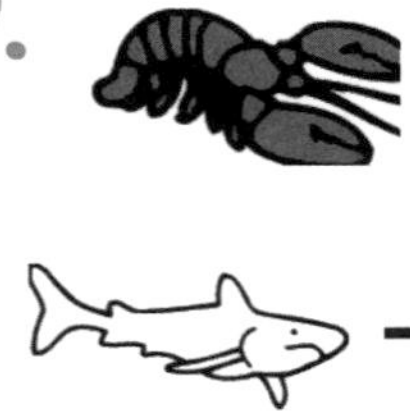 ☐
   ☐
   –
   _____
   ☐

8.  ☐
   ☐
   –
   _____
   ☐

9.  ☐
   ☐
   –
   _____
   ☐

Colouring
Key

dark blue

pink

dark gray

light gray

light blue

dark
brown

white

brown

peach

black

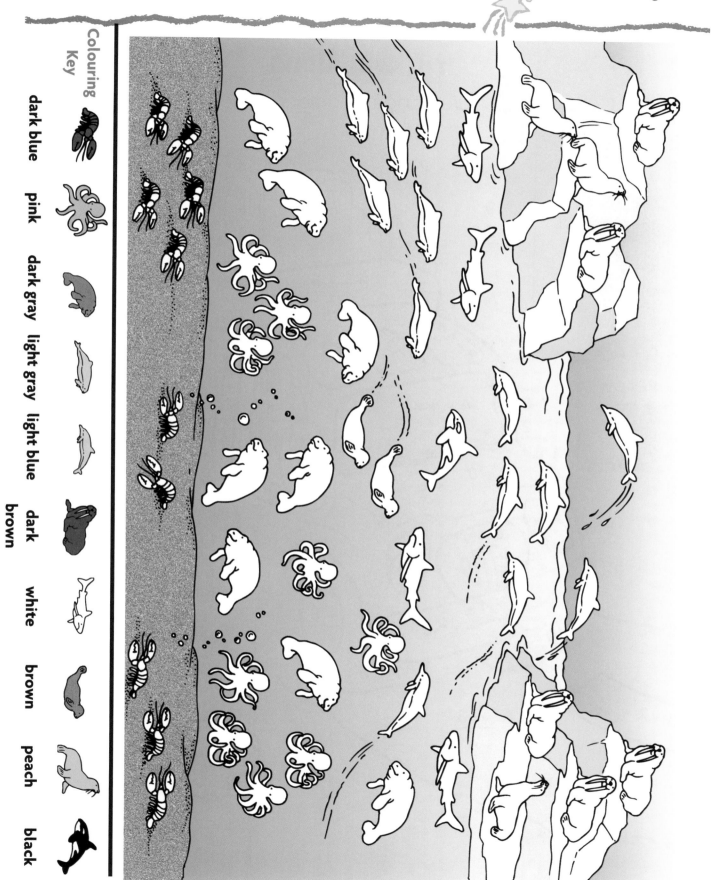

Name _____

Trucking Along

Subtract. Colour the picture using the colour code.

Colour Code

0	white
1	brown
2	black
3	green
4	purple
5	orange
6	yellow
7	blue
8	red

$$9 - 2$$

$$7 - 6 =$$

$$9 - 1 =$$

$$8 - 4 =$$

$$7 - 3 =$$

$$6 - 2 =$$

$$10 - 6$$

$$9 - 5$$

$$4 - 4 =$$

$$1 - 1$$

$$5 - 2$$

$$10 - 7$$

$$10 - 2 =$$

$$10 - 4 =$$

$$8 - 2$$

$$10 - 9$$

$$6 - 3 =$$

$$9 - 7 =$$

$$9 - 4 =$$

$$9 - 3$$

$$10 - 8 =$$

$$9 - 6$$

$$7 - 5 =$$

$$8 - 2 =$$

$$4 - 3$$

$$9 - 1$$

Night Lights

Subtract. Connect the dots from greatest to least.

$10 - 3 =$ ☐ •

$9 - 1 =$ ☐ •

$10 - 1 =$ ☐ •

$8 - 2 =$ ☐ •

$9 - 4 =$ ☐

$10 - 0 =$ ☐ •

$7 - 3 =$ ☐ •

$5 - 3 =$ ☐ •

$6 - 5 =$ ☐ •

$8 - 5 =$ ☐ •

Subtract. Connect the dots from least to greatest.

$10 - 0 =$ ☐ • - - - • $9 - 8 =$ ☐

$7 - 5 =$ ☐ •

$10 - 1 =$ ☐ •

$10 - 7 =$ ☐ •

$10 - 2 =$ ☐ •

The top picture gives off its own light. Colour this picture orange. The bottom picture reflects light from the sun. Colour this picture yellow.

$7 - 0 =$ ☐ •

$6 - 2 =$ ☐ •

$9 - 3 =$ ☐ •

$9 - 4 =$ ☐ •

Hop to It: Add and Subtract

Add or subtract. Trace the number line with your finger to check your work.

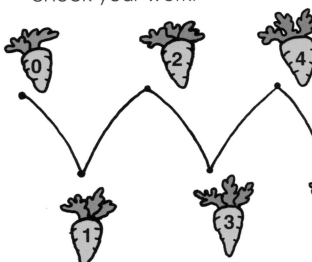

Examples: **4 + 5 = _____**

Start on **4**.

Move **5** 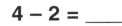 right.

4 − 2 = _____

Start on **4**.

Move **2** left.

7 − 3 = _____	9 − 6 = _____	2 + 0 = _____
5 + 5 = _____	8 − 7 = _____	4 + 3 = _____
10 − 4 = _____	6 + 2 = _____	7 − 2 = _____

 Circle the answer to each question.

What direction did move to add?   left   or   right

What direction did move to subtract?   left   or   right

Mitten Matchup

Add or subtract. Draw a line to match mittens with the same answer.

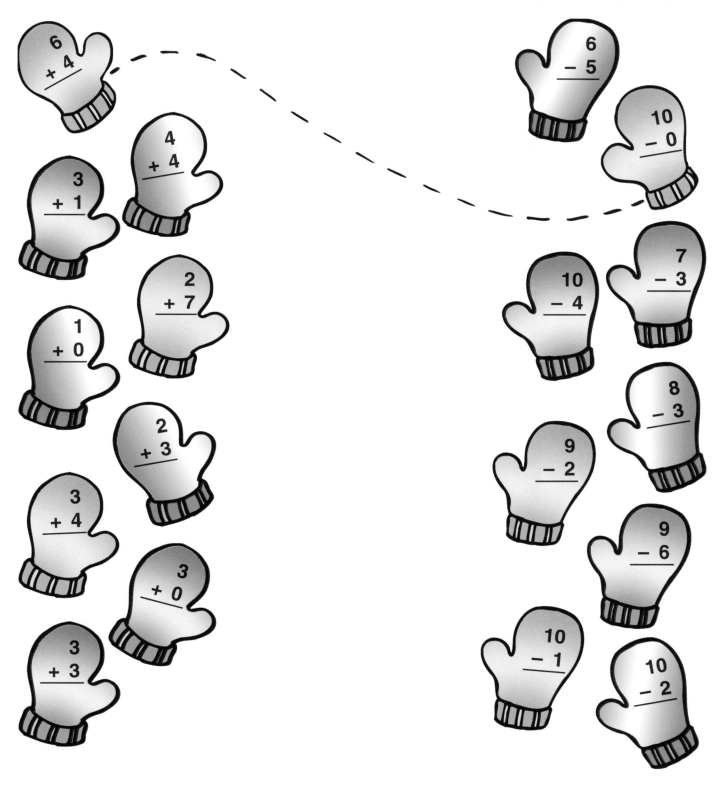

Blast Off

Add or subtract. Then use the code to answer the riddle below.

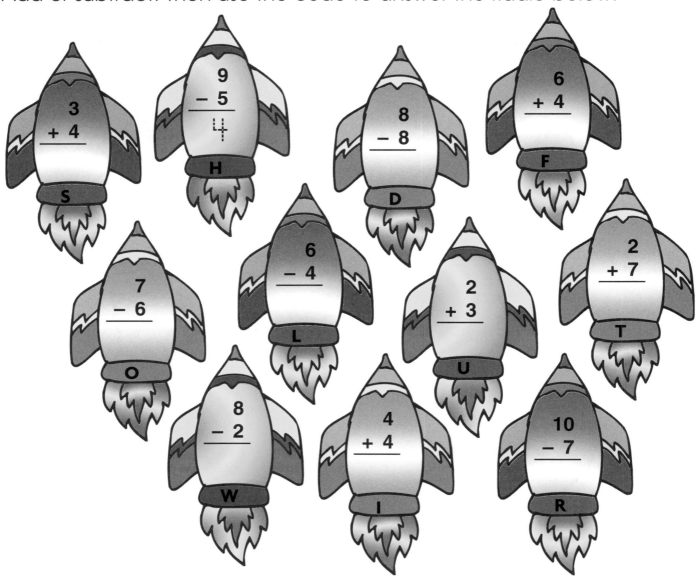

$$\begin{array}{r} 3 \\ + 4 \\ \hline \end{array}$$ S

$$\begin{array}{r} 9 \\ - 5 \\ \hline 4 \end{array}$$ H

$$\begin{array}{r} 8 \\ - 8 \\ \hline \end{array}$$ D

$$\begin{array}{r} 6 \\ + 4 \\ \hline \end{array}$$ F

$$\begin{array}{r} 7 \\ - 6 \\ \hline \end{array}$$ O

$$\begin{array}{r} 6 \\ - 4 \\ \hline \end{array}$$ L

$$\begin{array}{r} 2 \\ + 3 \\ \hline \end{array}$$ U

$$\begin{array}{r} 2 \\ + 7 \\ \hline \end{array}$$ T

$$\begin{array}{r} 8 \\ - 2 \\ \hline \end{array}$$ W

$$\begin{array}{r} 4 \\ + 4 \\ \hline \end{array}$$ I

$$\begin{array}{r} 10 \\ - 7 \\ \hline \end{array}$$ R

How is an astronaut's job unlike any other job?

___ ___ ___ '   ___ ___ ___   ___ ___
 8   9   7   1   5   9   1   10

___ H ___ ___   ___ ___ ___ ___ ___!
 9   4 8   7   6   1   3   2   0

Out on the Town

Colour a box on the graph for each item in the picture.

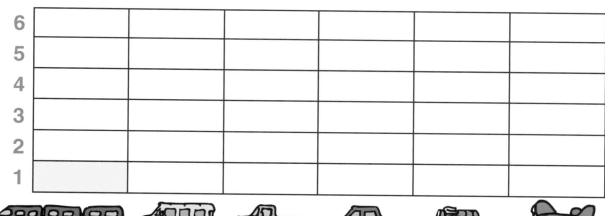

A. How many 🚗 and ✈️ altogether? _6_ ⊕ _2_ = _8_

B. How many 🏍️ and 🚂 in all? ____ + ____ = ____

C. How many more 🚗 than 🚌 ? ____ + ____ = ____

Shapes on a Snake

Add or subtract.

A. 🤍 6 + 4 = 10

B. ▢ − ◇ = _____

C. ⬤ − ⬡ = _____

D. ⬭ − 🤍 = _____

E. ▭ + ⬡ = _____

F. ⬡ + ⬡ = _____

G. ◇ + ⬡ = _____

H. 🤍 + ⬭ = _____

I. △ − ▭ = _____

J. ▢ − ⬡ = _____

Planes . . . Trains . . .

Add or subtract.

A. There are **7** cars in the parking lot. Then **3** more cars park there, too. How many cars are there in all in the lot?

__7__ (+) __3__ = __10__ cars

B. There are **7** boxes on the truck. Then **4** boxes fall on the street. How many boxes are left on the truck?

____ +
____ − ____ = ____ boxes

C. There are **10** planes waiting on the runway. Then **6** planes take off. How many planes are left on the runway?

____ +
____ − ____ = ____ planes

D. There are **8** girls and **2** boys on the bus. How many more girls than boys are on the bus?

____ +
____ − ____ = ____ more girls

E. There are **5** people in the first car and **4** people in the second car. How many people in all?

____ +
____ − ____ = ____ people

Name _____

Slice It Up

Add. Colour the picture using the colour code.

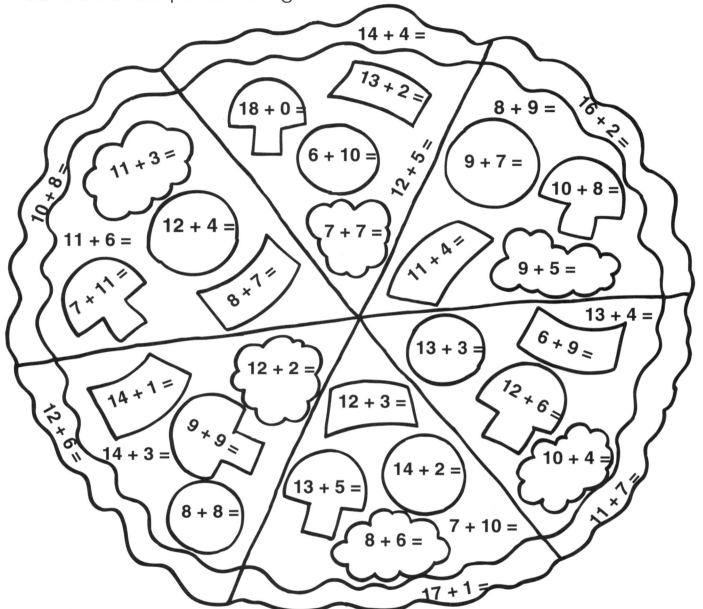

Colour Code	brown	green	red	yellow	tan
	14	15	16	17	18

How many different ways can you make a sum of 10? Show your work on another piece of paper.

Leap on Over

Add. To show the frog's path across the pond, colour each lily pad green if the sum is greater than 10.

10 + 1 =

6 + 4 =

6 + 9 =

5 + 2 =

7 + 0 =

5 + 5 =

9 + 2 =

10 + 4 =

3 + 7 =

7 + 6 =

4 + 3 =

5 + 4 =

3 + 8 =

2 + 2 =

8 + 8 =

How many leaps did the frog take across the pond? _____

Animal Mystery

What kind of animal always carries a trunk?

_____

To find out, solve the addition problems. If the answer is greater than 9, colour the shape yellow. If the answer is less than 10, colour the shape grey.

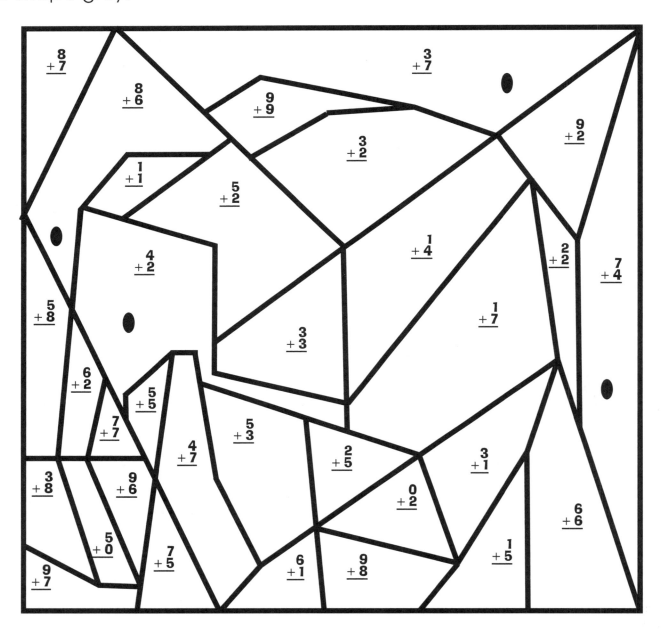

Scarecrow Sam

Why doesn't Scarecrow Sam tell secrets when he is near Farmer Joe's bean patch? _____

To find out the answer, add the numbers. Circle the pumpkins that have sums of 14, and write the letters that appear inside those pumpkins in the boxes below.

Flying High

Add down and across to find the missing number.

A.

2	4	6
3	1	4
5	5	10

B.

4	1	
7	3	

C.

6	7	
2	1	

D.

5	6	
4	3	

E.

2	6	
5	0	

F.

4	7	
3	3	

Double Dips

Write the double to equal the number on the cone.

Circle the answer.

When adding doubles, the sum will always be: even   odd

Not Far From Home

Start at . Write the number of steps. Add.

steps to + steps home = _____ steps   **steps to + steps home = _____ steps**

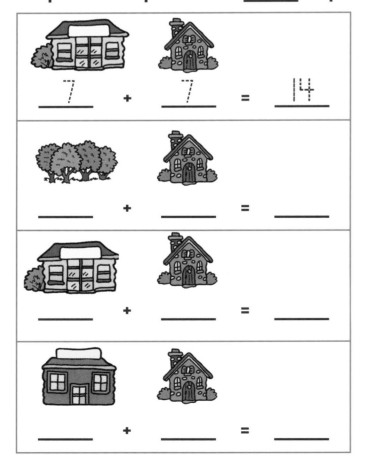 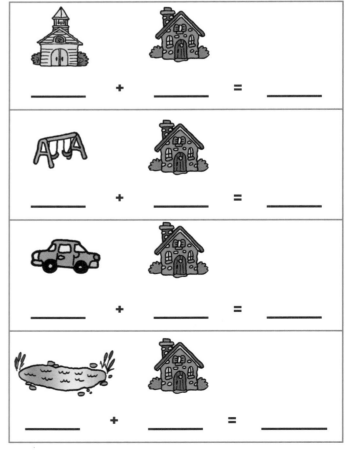

Break the Code

Subtract.

A. 6
− 2

B. 13
− 7

C. 17
− 7

D. 18
− 9

E. 15
− 8

F. 11
− 9

G. 9
− 4

H. 14
− 6

I. 11
− 8

J. 7
− 6

Use the answers above to solve each problem.

K.

L.

M.

N.

O.

P.

Q.

Name _____

The Big Search

Subtract. Circle the difference.

11 – 7 = five three (four)	**14 – 9 =** nine one five
13 – 6 = six nine seven	**16 – 5 =** twelve thirteen eleven
18 – 9 = eleven ten nine	**17 – 11 =** seven six ten
15 – 5 = ten seven five	**12 – 9 =** three two four
12 – 4 = six eight nine	**11 – 9 =** three five two

Find each circled number in the word puzzle. Look → and ↓.

```
(f  o  u  r)  h  i  o  n  e  g  s  k  m
 i  f  o  n  t  g  y  f  a  f  u  e  z
 f  t  l  u  e  j  s  i  x  s  b  x  t
 t  t  w  e  l  v  e  v  k  s  t  l  h
 e  p  n  i  n  e  w  e  j  e  r  t  i
 e  d  n  g  q  i  h  r  y  v  a  q  r
 n  v  h  h  o  t  h  r  e  e  c  s  t
 d  m  k  t  c  w  b  t  e  n  t  r  e
 x  d  i  p  g  o  a  c  p  f  i  s  e
 c  e  l  e  v  e  n  a  b  z  o  v  n
 b  w  u  d  i  f  f  e  r  e  n  c  e
```

 See if you can find these number words: twelve, fifteen, thirteen, subtraction, difference.

Race Through the Facts

Add or subtract. The race car that ends with the highest number wins the race!

$7 + 2 =$ ___ $- 4 =$ ___ $- 3 =$ ___ $+ 9 =$ ___

$12 - 3 =$ ___ $- 6 =$ ___ $+ 2 =$ ___ $+ 9 =$ ___ $+ 5 =$ ___ $- 8 =$ ___ $+ 4 =$ ___ $+ 6 =$ ___ $- 9 =$ ___ $+ 6 =$ ___ $+ 1 =$ ___

$- 9 =$ ___ $+ 7 =$ ___ $+ 3 =$ ___ $- 2 =$ ___ $+ 4 =$ ___ $+ 1 =$ ___ $+ 7 =$ ___ $- 8 =$ ___ $+ 1 =$ ___ $- 11 =$ ___ $- 5 =$ ___ $+ 13 =$ ___ $- 7 =$ ___ $+ 3 =$ ___

$+ 2 =$ ___ $+ 3 =$ ___ $- 3 =$ ___

 Colour the winning race car blue.

Little Snacks

Add or subtract. Then follow the maze through the even answers.

Start

2 + 2 =

16 − 9 =

4 + 5 =

13 − 6 =

14 − 8 =

10 − 7 =

13 − 5 =

9 + 4 =

3 + 7 =

15 − 6 =

16 − 6 =

11 + 3 =

17 − 8 =

7 + 5 =

18 − 6 =

8 + 3 =

5 + 2 =

9 + 9 =

The elephant found 9 peanuts. He ate 6 peanuts.
How many peanuts are left? _____

Name _____

Flying Families

Fill in the missing number for each family. Use the numbers from the box.

9	12	15	8	10
6	4	7	5	11	2

💡 **Fill in the families with twins.**

Colourful Flowers

Colour a box on the graph for each item in the picture.

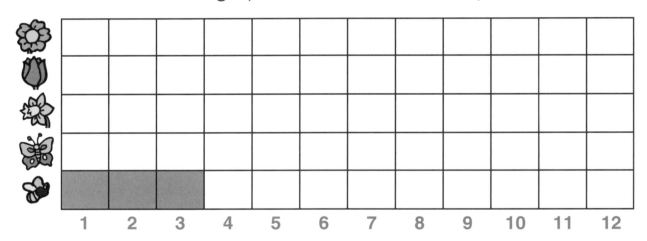

| | 1 | 2 | 3 | 4 | 5 | 6 | 7 | 8 | 9 | 10 | 11 | 12 |

A. Which flower is found the most?

B. How many and altogether? _____ + _____ = _____

C. How many more than ? _____ − _____ = _____

D. How many insects in all? _____ + _____ = _____

E. How many more than ? _____ − _____ = _____

F. How many and altogether? _____ + _____ = _____

A Nutty Bunch

Add or subtract. Colour the nut brown if the answer matches
the squirrel.

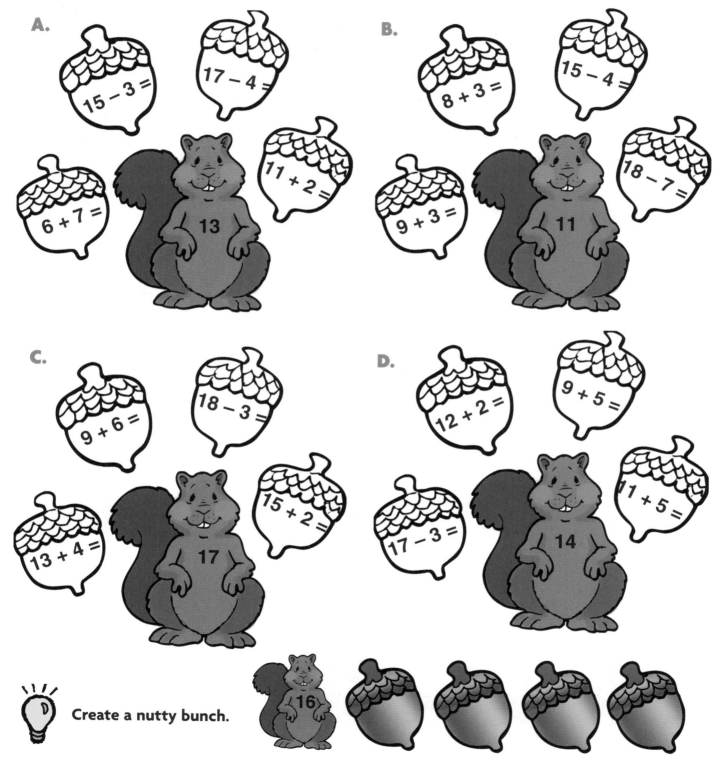

Create a nutty bunch.

Penguin Parade

Add or subtract. Write the pattern on the flag.

Row 1:
5 + 7
8 + 3
15 − 5
18 − 9
11 − 3
12 − 5

Row 2:
9 − 7
12 − 8
5 + 1
16 − 8
13 − 3
7 + 5

Row 3:
12 − 9
11 − 5
13 − 4
7 + 5
18 − 3
11 + 7

Row 4:
15 − 2
4 + 7
12 − 3
12 − 5
8 − 3
12 − 9

A Perfect Strike

Fill in the missing number.

2 1 3

9 3

16

4 3

9

5 2

10

2 7

14

2 5

11

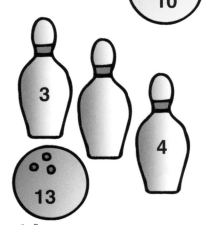

3 4

13

5 3

12

5 3

18

 Find three different ways to make 8 with 3 numbers.

8

What a Treat!

Find the number in the mouse and cheese. ☐

Find the sum of the numbers in the cheese.

_____ + _____ + _____ = _____

Find the sum of the numbers in the mouse.

_____ + _____ + _____ = _____

Find the number in the
rabbit and carrot. ☐

Find the sum of the largest number in the
rabbit and the smallest number in the carrot.

_____ + _____ = _____

Find the difference between the largest
and smallest number in the carrot.

_____ – _____ = _____

 Find the sum of all the numbers in the mouse and cheese.

_____ + _____ + _____ + _____ + _____ = _____

Find the sum of all the numbers in the rabbit and carrot.

_____ + _____ + _____ + _____ + _____ = _____

Have a Heart

Circle a group of 10. Write the number of tens and ones.

tens	ones

tens	ones

tens	ones

tens	ones

tens	ones

tens	ones

tens	ones

tens	ones

Beautiful Butterflies

Add. Colour the picture using the colour code.

Colour Code

26	red
29	orange
38	green
54	purple
87	yellow

86
+ 1

54
+ 0

37
+ 1

24
+ 2

50
+ 4

80
+ 7

31
+ 7

50
+ 4

23
+ 6

25
+ 1

51
+ 3

24
+ 5

21
+ 8

26
+ 0

34
+ 4

21
+ 5

30
+ 8

23
+ 3

53
+ 1

52
+ 2

85
+ 2

20
+ 6

83
+ 4

84
+ 3

81
+ 6

23
+ 6

22
+ 7

Most adult butterflies live for about   11
                                          + 3   **days.**

Where's the Beach?

Add. To find the path to the beach, colour each box with an odd answer yellow.

14 + 3	34 + 2	81 + 3

76 + 2	25 + 4	56 + 3	11 + 3	40 + 8

| 87
+ 1 | 22
+ 2 | 32
+ 3 | 65
+ 1 | 93
+ 5 |

| 10
+ 8 | 41
+ 2 | 70
+ 7 | 32
+ 6 | 84
+ 4 |

| 73
+ 5 | 63
+ 2 | 55
+ 1 | 41
+ 5 | 23
+ 3 |

98 + 1	53 + 4	82 + 5

By the Seashore

Use the code below to write each missing number. Add.

93

+ _____

82
+ _____

14

+ _____

21
+ _____

53
+ _____

45

+ _____

73
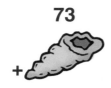
+ _____

36
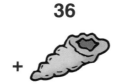
+ _____

61
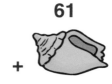
+ _____

32
+ _____

Find the sum for all the shells. _____ + _____ + _____ + _____ + _____ = _____

Name _____

Sail Away

Finish each addition sentence. Add.

+5	
	+5 = 38
94	

+2	
87	
16	
24	

+6	
20	
52	
91	

+3	
94	33
26	
45	61

+4	
55	
32	
83	

+	
24	26
18	20
95	97

💡 **Fill in the empty flag!**

Dino-Math

Subtract. Colour the picture using the colour code.

Colour Code

16	red
22	orange
34	purple
57	blue
73	yellow
85	green

Number Buddies

Subtract. Remember: the largest number always goes on top!

A. 7   39 $\begin{array}{c} 3\ 9 \\ -\ \ 7 \\ \hline \end{array}$

B. 54   1

C. 87   6

D. 73   3

E. 25   4

F. 42   2

G. 7   98

H. 5   66

💡 **Fill in each missing number.**

39   35   4

27   20

88   83

Name _____

Treasure Island

Subtract.

43 − 1	95 − 5	79 − 3	36 − 4	89 − 7	66 − 3	83 − 2
59 − 9	37 − 2	24 − 3	27 − 6	42 − 1	90 − 0	55 − 2
33 − 3	84 − 4	28 − 8	71 − 1	62 − 2	68 − 3	77 − 3

Use the clues to find the gold, the ship, and the treasure in the boxes above.

Find the gold.

The difference is greater than **50** and less than **55**. Colour the box with the gold yellow.

Find the ship.

The difference is greater than **30** and less than **35**. Colour the box with the ship orange.

Find the sunken treasure.

The difference is greater than **70** and less than **75**. Colour the box with the treasure red.

Riding on Air

Add. Colour the picture using the colour code.

42
+ 53

31
+ 23

24 + 13 =

46
+ 32

23
+ 55

64
+ 14

60
+ 18

65
+ 21

24
+ 62

75
+ 11

53
+ 33

24
+ 30

15 + 22 =

42
+ 12

11 + 13 =

54
+ 32

42
+ 36

15
+ 22

72 + 23 =

25 + 24 =

36 + 13 =

37 + 12 =

Colour Code

24	red
37	blue
49	brown
54	white
78	yellow
86	purple
95	green

Number Puzzler

Can you spell 80 in two letters?

To find out how, do the addition problems. If the answer is even, shade the square. If your answers are correct, the shaded squares will spell the answer.

12 + 13	24 + 34	22 + 21	77 + 22	35 + 43	52 + 12	40 + 52
11 + 31	30 + 39	46 + 52	15 + 12	10 + 71	63 + 11	13 + 80
36 + 32	30 + 10	11 + 11	15 + 4	20 + 21	15 + 11	22 + 33
14 + 14	13 + 16	10 + 20	14 + 25	11 + 20	15 + 21	20 + 31
36 + 52	21 + 32	10 + 50	44 + 41	24 + 43	31 + 21	13 + 82

Colour the Sunflower

Do the addition problems in the sunflower picture below. Then use the Colour Key to tell you what colour to make each answer.

Extra: Write your age on four flashcards, and then add a 6, 7, 8, and 9 to each of the cards. Practice the answers with a friend.

Colour Key
56 = green
68 = orange
89 = yellow
97 = blue

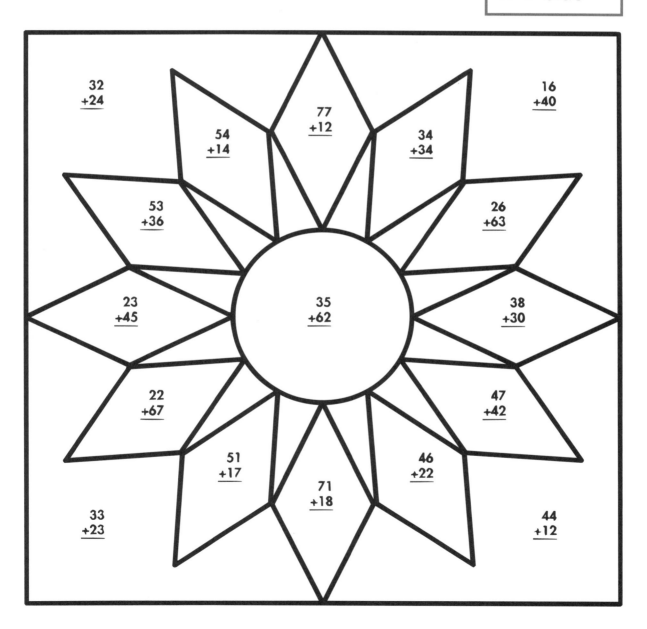

Roger the Rooster

Why did Roger the Rooster decide not to get in a barnyard fight?

_____

To find out, add the numbers and shade the blocks as described below.

Shade the squares in row 1 that contain answers less than 25.

Shade the squares in row 2 that contain odd-numbered answers.

Shade the squares in row 3 that contain answers greater than 35.

Shade the squares in row 4 that contain even-numbered answers.

Shade the squares in row 5 that contain answers that end in zero.

$13 + 11$ **H**	$26 + 33$ **Y**	$16 + 31$ **O**	$10 + 12$ **E**	$64 + 24$ **U**
$20 + 15$ **W**	$71 + 12$ **A**	$25 + 21$ **W**	$51 + 10$ **S**	$22 + 16$ **O**
$22 + 10$ **L**	$14 + 14$ **C**	$20 + 10$ **E**	$25 + 31$ **A**	$21 + 3$ **L**
$42 + 30$ **C**	$13 + 43$ **H**	$54 + 15$ **F**	$21 + 61$ **I**	$61 + 33$ **C**
$10 + 30$ **K**	$20 + 30$ **E**	$16 + 32$ **J**	$71 + 23$ **S**	$70 + 20$ **N**

Baseball Puzzle

What animal can always be found at a baseball game?

_____

To find out, do the subtraction problems. If the answer is greater than 9, colour the shapes black. If the answer is less than 10, colour the shapes red.

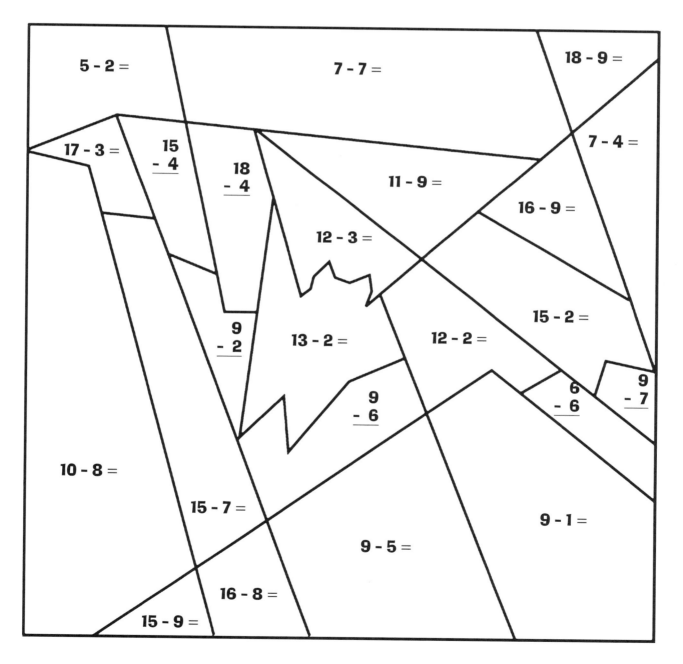

5 - 2 =

7 - 7 =

18 - 9 =

17 - 3 =

15
- 4

18
- 4

11 - 9 =

7 - 4 =

16 - 9 =

12 - 3 =

9
- 2

13 - 2 =

12 - 2 =

15 - 2 =

9
- 6

6
- 6

9
- 7

10 - 8 =

15 - 7 =

9 - 1 =

9 - 5 =

16 - 8 =

15 - 9 =

Colour the Bowtie

Do the subtraction problems in the picture below. Then use the Colour Key to tell you what colour to make each answer.

Extra: On the back of this sheet of paper, draw a picture of four of your friends or family members. Give each one a bowtie!

Colour Key
14 = red
26 = purple
33 = blue
47 = yellow
63 = green

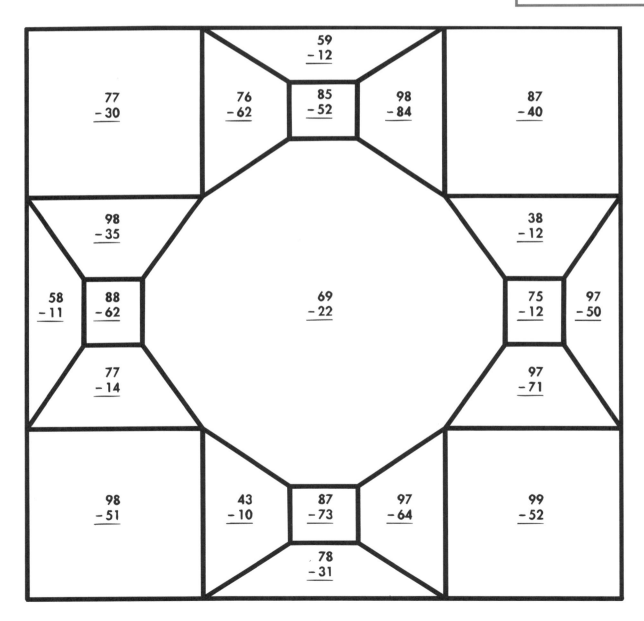

Detective Work

Use the code to help Detective Dave discover the secret phone number. The first problem has been done for you.

1	2	3
4	5	6
7	8	9

1.

$7 - 1 = 6$

2.

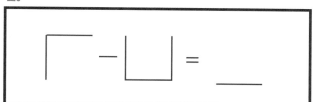

3.

$\boxed{\ } - \boxed{\ } = \underline{\ }$

4.

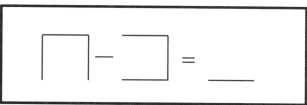

5.

$\boxed{\ } - \boxed{\ } = \underline{\ }$

6.

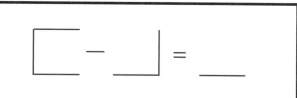

7.

$\boxed{\ } - \boxed{\ } = \underline{\ }$

The phone number is:

__ __ __ - __ __ __ __

Name _____

Have a Ball

Subtract.

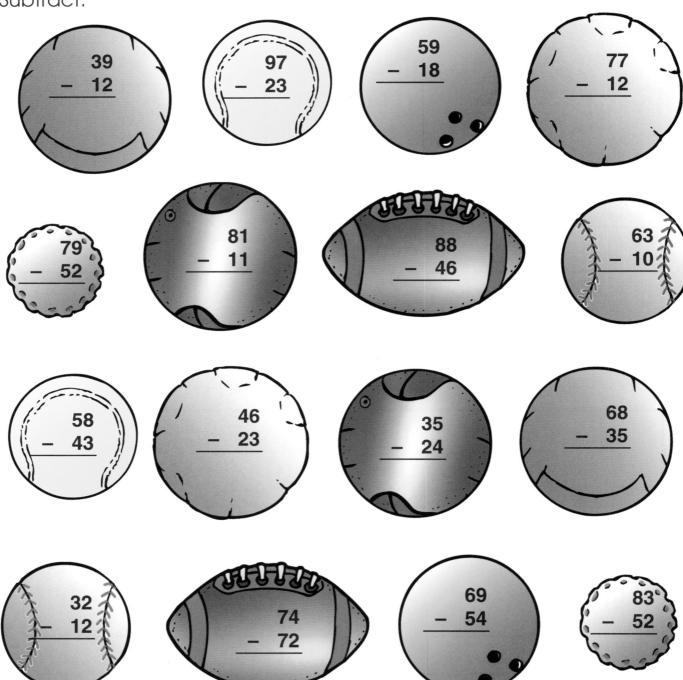

39 − 12

97 − 23

59 − 18

77 − 12

79 − 52

81 − 11

88 − 46

63 − 10

58 − 43

46 − 23

35 − 24

68 − 35

32 − 12

74 − 72

69 − 54

83 − 52

 The Rams scored 49 points in the football game. The Bears scored 27 points.
How many more points did the Rams score than the Bears? _____

Opposites Attract

Add or subtract. Connect the magnets that have the same answer.

42
+ 33

new

close
79
− 32

32
+ 54

laugh

old
99
− 24

35
+ 12

open

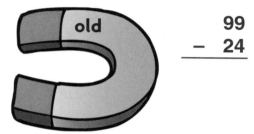
left
99
− 10

13
+ 10

sink

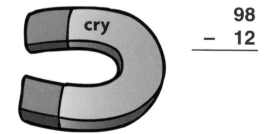
cry
98
− 12

37
+ 52

right

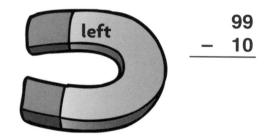
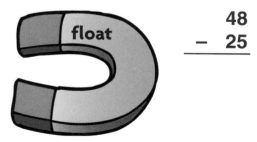
float
48
− 25

On another piece of paper, write an addition and subtraction problem which have the same answer.

How Much Money?

52¢

34¢

13¢

75¢

47¢

21¢

62¢

10¢

Add to find out how much.

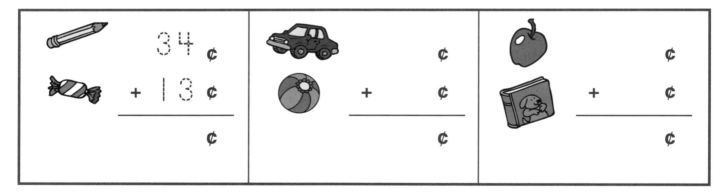

	3 4 ¢			¢			¢
	+ 1 3 ¢		+	¢		+	¢
	____ ¢			¢			¢

Subtract to find out how much.

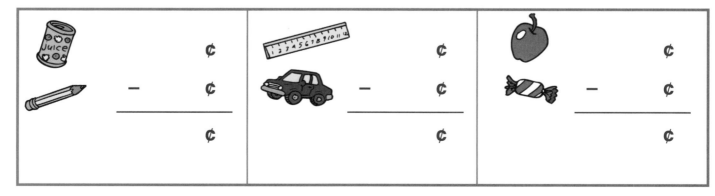

	¢		¢		¢
−	¢	−	¢	−	¢
	¢		¢		¢

Snuggle Up With a Book

Day of the Week	Reading Minutes
Sunday	97
Monday	28
Tuesday	73
Wednesday	44
Thursday	51
Friday	45
Saturday	80

Use the chart to answer the questions.

A. What day did Alex read for the longest time?

_____

B. How many minutes did Alex read on Wednesday and Friday? _____ minutes

C. What day did Alex read for the shortest time?

_____

D. How many more minutes did Alex read on Sunday than Tuesday? _____ minutes

E. How many minutes did Alex read on Monday and Thursday? _____ minutes

F. How many more minutes did Alex read on Tuesday than Thursday? _____ minutes

One hour is 60 minutes. On what days did Alex read longer than one hour?

_____ , _____ , _____

Let the Sun Shine

Add or subtract. Then use the code to fill in the letters to finish each sun fact.

13	26	34	42	57	63	71	76	85	88
f	a	s	g	r	e	l	h	t	i

$$\begin{array}{r} 13 \\ +\,21 \\ \hline \end{array} \qquad \begin{array}{r} 32 \\ +\,53 \\ \hline \end{array} \qquad \begin{array}{r} 57 \\ -\,31 \\ \hline \end{array} \qquad \begin{array}{r} 89 \\ -\,32 \\ \hline \end{array}$$

The sun is a ____ ____ ____ ____ .

$$\begin{array}{r} 30 \\ +\,41 \\ \hline \end{array} \quad \begin{array}{r} 98 \\ -\,10 \\ \hline \end{array} \quad \begin{array}{r} 12 \\ +\,30 \\ \hline \end{array} \quad \begin{array}{r} 97 \\ -\,21 \\ \hline \end{array} \quad \begin{array}{r} 99 \\ -\,14 \\ \hline \end{array}$$

The sun gives ____ ____ ____ ____ ____ and

$$\begin{array}{r} 34 \\ +\,42 \\ \hline \end{array} \quad \begin{array}{r} 51 \\ +\,12 \\ \hline \end{array} \quad \begin{array}{r} 88 \\ -\,62 \\ \hline \end{array} \quad \begin{array}{r} 42 \\ +\,43 \\ \hline \end{array}$$

____ ____ ____ ____ to Earth.

$$\begin{array}{r} 88 \\ -\,17 \\ \hline \end{array} \quad \begin{array}{r} 56 \\ +\,32 \\ \hline \end{array} \quad \begin{array}{r} 49 \\ -\,36 \\ \hline \end{array} \quad \begin{array}{r} 30 \\ +\,33 \\ \hline \end{array}$$

Without the sun, there would be no ____ ____ ____ ____ .

Animal Surprises

Add or subtract. Match the answer to the animal fact.

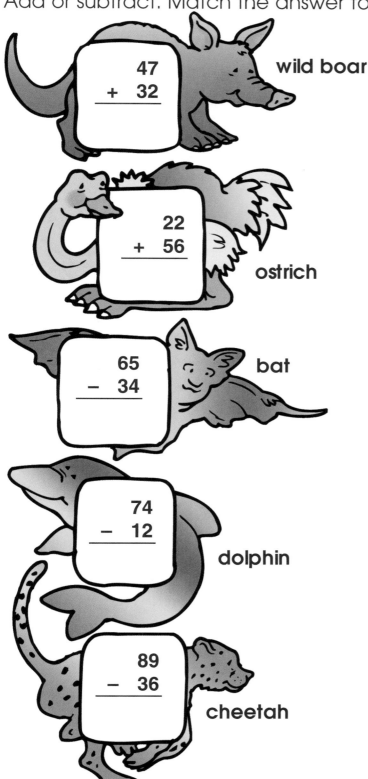

wild boar

$$\begin{array}{r} 47 \\ +\ 32 \\ \hline \end{array}$$

ostrich

$$\begin{array}{r} 22 \\ +\ 56 \\ \hline \end{array}$$

bat

$$\begin{array}{r} 65 \\ -\ 34 \\ \hline \end{array}$$

dolphin

$$\begin{array}{r} 74 \\ -\ 12 \\ \hline \end{array}$$

cheetah

$$\begin{array}{r} 89 \\ -\ 36 \\ \hline \end{array}$$

(31) I am the only mammal that can fly.

(78) I am a large bird, but I cannot fly.

(79) I can weigh over 150 kilograms.

(53) I am the fastest of all animals.

(62) I swim like a fish, but I am really a mammal.

Fishbowl

Add or subtract. Circle the fish that
does not belong with the family.
Hint: Look at the tens place.

Make another family with 7 in the
tens place.

Scholastic Success With

MATH

Colour the Basket

Count the number of dots or triangles in each shape. Then use the Colour Key to tell you what colour to make each shape. (For example, a shape with 7 dots will be coloured green.)

Extra: On the back of this sheet of paper, draw a basket filled with six things you would carry in it.

Colour Key
6 = yellow
7 = green
8 = brown
9 = red
10 = green

Number User

I use numbers to tell about myself.

1. _____
MY STREET NUMBER

2. _____
MY ZIP CODE

3. _____
MY TELEPHONE NUMBER

4. _____
MY BIRTHDAY

5. _____
MY AGE

6. _____
MY HEIGHT AND WEIGHT

7. _____
NUMBER OF PEOPLE IN MY FAMILY

I CAN COUNT UP TO

8. _____

Frog School

At Frog School, Croaker Frog and his friends sit on lily pads.

Are there enough lily pads for all the frogs in Croaker's class?
Yes _____ No _____

Draw lines to match the frogs with the lily pads.

 How many frogs need lily pads? _____.

Odd and Even Patterns

A pattern can have two things repeating. This is called an "AB" pattern.

1. Look around the classroom. What "AB" patterns do you see? Draw one "AB" pattern in the box.

2. Use red and blue crayons to colour the numbers in the chart using an "AB" pattern.

Hundred's Chart

1	2	3	4	5	6	7	8	9	10
11	12	13	14	15	16	17	18	19	20
21	22	23	24	25	26	27	28	29	30
31	32	33	34	35	36	37	38	39	40
41	42	43	44	45	46	47	48	49	50
51	52	53	54	55	56	57	58	59	60
61	62	63	64	65	66	67	68	69	70
71	72	73	74	75	76	77	78	79	80
81	82	83	84	85	86	87	88	89	90
91	92	93	94	95	96	97	98	99	100

Use this rule:
   1 = red
   2 = blue
   3 = red
   4 = blue, and so on

The blue numbers are **even numbers**. They can be split evenly into 2 whole numbers.

The red numbers are **odd numbers**. They cannot be split evenly into 2 whole numbers.

Classroom Garage Sale

Tolu's class did some spring cleaning. Then they had a garage sale. They sorted the things they were selling. Sort these objects into like groups. Draw the items of each group on one of the tables below.

Below each table, write a label for the group.

Flowers in a Pot

Count the dots in the boxes. Then colour the matching number word.

 green •• yellow

••• red :: purple

:: blue

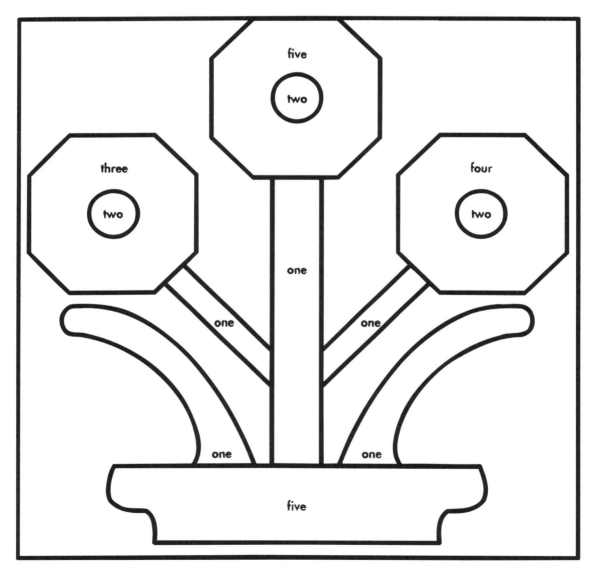

five

two

three

two

four

two

one

one

one

one

one

five

💡 **Use bright colours to draw a pot of flowers on another sheet of paper.**

Sign Shape

Street signs come in different shapes. Use string to form the shapes below. Work with a partner. Answer the questions below about the shapes, too.

What shape is this sign? _____

How many sides does it have? _____

What shape is this sign? _____

How many sides does it have? _____

What shape is this sign? _____

How many sides does it have? _____

What shape is this sign? _____

How many sides does it have? _____

Bird Feeder Geometry

It's spring! The birds are coming back. Kwaku and his mother made two bird feeders.

What shapes can you find on their feeders? Write your ideas on the lines. _____

_____

Shape Study

"Symmetry" exists when the two halves of something are mirror images of each other.

Look at the pictures below. Colour those that show symmetry.
(Hint: Imagine the pictures are folded on the dotted lines.)

Complete the drawings below. Connect the dots to show the other
half. (Hint: The pictures are symmetrical!)

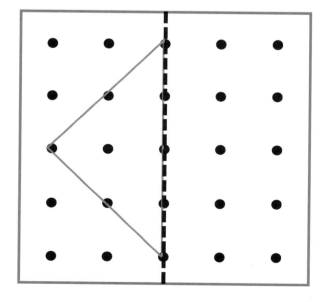
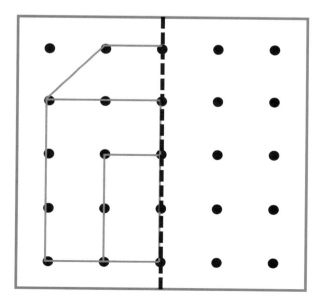

Picking Out Patterns

On the 100th day of school, everyone in Pat's class picked out patterns on the 100 Chart. Look at the chart below.

1	2	3	4	5	6	7	8	9	10
11	12	13	14	15	16	17	18	19	20
21	22	23	24	25	26	27	28	29	30
31	32	33	34	35	36	37	38	39	40
41	42	43	44	45	46	47	48	49	50
51	52	53	54	55	56	57	58	59	60
61	62	63	64	65	66	67	68	69	70
71	72	73	74	75	76	77	78	79	80
81	82	83	84	85	86	87	88	89	90
91	92	93	94	95	96	97	98	99	100

Find and finish the pattern starting with 2, 12, 22

_____

Find and finish the pattern starting with 100, 90, 80

_____

Find and finish the pattern starting with 97, 87, 77

_____

Find and finish the pattern starting with 11, 22, 33

_____

Mystery Critter

I climb up the side of walls and never fall.

I am a fast runner and have a very long tail. Who am I? _____

To find out, connect the numbers in order from 20 to 68.

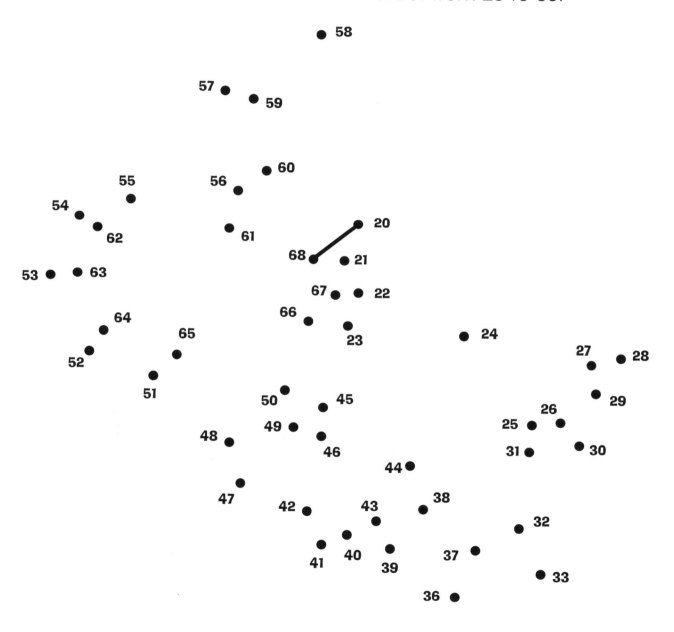

Snowflakes on Mittens

Estimate how many snowflakes are on each mitten.
For the first mitten, skip count by 2s to find out.
(You can circle groups of 2.)
For the second mitten, skip count by 5s to check your answer.
(You can circle groups of 5.)

 Would snowflakes really wait for you to count?

Explain your answer:

Patterns of Five

Look at the number chart below. Starting with 1, count 5 squares. Colour in the fifth square. Then count 5 more squares and colour in the fifth square. Keep going until you reach 100.

Hundred's Chart

1	2	3	4	5	6	7	8	9	10
11	12	13	14	15	16	17	18	19	20
21	22	23	24	25	26	27	28	29	30
31	32	33	34	35	36	37	38	39	40
41	42	43	44	45	46	47	48	49	50
51	52	53	54	55	56	57	58	59	60
61	62	63	64	65	66	67	68	69	70
71	72	73	74	75	76	77	78	79	80
81	82	83	84	85	86	87	88	89	90
91	92	93	94	95	96	97	98	99	100

Tally marks can be arranged in groups of five, like this:
Then you can count by fives.

Count how many girls and boys are in your class. Draw tally marks in groups of five.

Girls: _____   Boys: _____

Now count the total number. Write the totals here:

Girls: _____   Boys: _____

Ladybug Dots

Every year, ladybugs hibernate when the weather gets cool. Count the dots on each ladybug wing. Then write an equation to show the total number of dots each ladybug has. The first one has been done for you.

3 + **3** = **6**

_____ + _____ = _____

_____ + _____ = _____

_____ + _____ = _____

_____ + _____ = _____

_____ + _____ = _____

 Write the sums in order, from lowest to highest.

_____ _____ _____ _____ _____

What pattern do you see?

_____

Pattern Block Design

How many total pieces are in this pattern block design?

2 + 2 + 1= _____

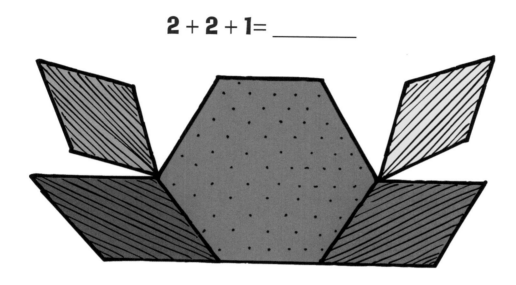

Now make your own design by drawing 5 pattern blocks. Connect the blocks to form a pattern different from the one above. You may want to use a block pattern more than once.

Write an equation to show how many of each shape you used.

Equation: _____

Coin-Toss Subtraction

Toss 3 coins. Write "H" for heads or "T" for tails in the circles below to show how the coins landed. Then finish each sentence to tell about your toss. Write a subtraction equation to show your toss, too. Write the number of heads first. We did the first one for you. Try it three times.

(**H**)(**H**)(**T**) There are ___more___ heads than tails.
                               (more/fewer)

Subtraction equation: ___3 coins___ - ___2 heads___ = ___1 tail___

◯◯◯ There are _____ heads than tails.
                          (more/fewer)

Subtraction equation: _____ - _____ = _____

◯◯◯ There are _____ heads than tails.
                          (more/fewer)

Subtraction equation: _____ - _____ = _____

◯◯◯ There are _____ heads than tails.
                          (more/fewer)

Subtraction equation: _____ - _____ = _____

What's Your Story?

Look at the equation below.

3 + 3 = 6

Make up a story to go with the equation.

Draw a picture in the box to go with your story.

Now write about your picture on the lines below.

_____

_____

_____

_____

_____

Coin-Toss Addition

Toss 6 coins. Write "H" for heads or "T" for tails in the circles below to show your toss. Then write the addition equation. Write the number of "heads" first. We did the first one for you. Try it five times.

(H)(H)(H)(H)(T)(T) Equation: **4 + 2 = 6** _____

◯ ◯ ◯ ◯ ◯ ◯ Equation: _____

◯ ◯ ◯ ◯ ◯ ◯ Equation: _____

◯ ◯ ◯ ◯ ◯ ◯ Equation: _____

◯ ◯ ◯ ◯ ◯ ◯ Equation: _____

◯ ◯ ◯ ◯ ◯ ◯ Equation: _____

Time to Get Up!

Twenty animals were hibernating near Sleepy Pond.
5 of them woke up. Colour 5 animals below.

How many are still sleeping? _____

A week later, 7 more woke up. Colour 7 other animals.

How many are still sleeping? _____

Money Matters

Alex asked his little brother Billy to trade piggy banks.

Alex's bank has these coins: Billy's has these coins:

Do you think this is a fair trade? _____

Test your answer:

Add up Alex's coins: _____

Add up Billy's coins: _____

Write the totals in this Greater Than/Less Than equation:

_____ > _____

Who has more money? _____

The Truth About the Tooth Fairy

Look at Ali Gator's teeth.

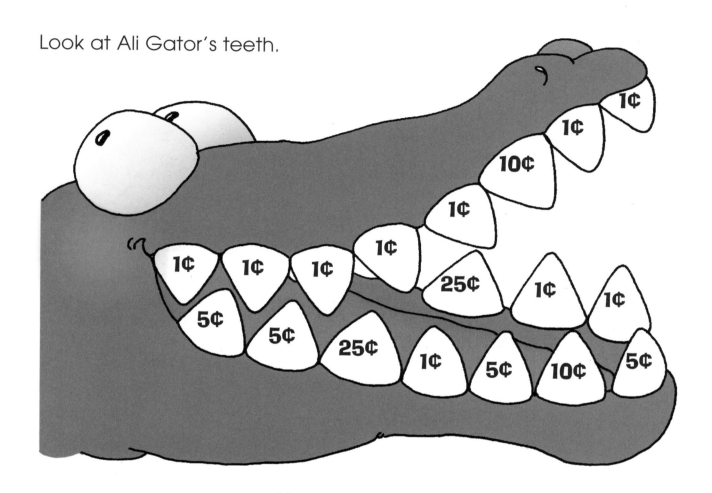

	How many teeth?	How much money in all?
1. How many 1¢?		cents
2. How many 5¢?		cents
3. How many 10¢?		cents
4. How many 25¢?		cents

Measuring Up

People didn't always measure with rulers. Long ago, Egyptians and other peoples measured objects with body parts. Try it!

A "digit" is the width of your middle finger at the top joint where it bends.

How many digits long is:

a pair of scissors? _____

a math book? _____

a crayon? _____

A "palm" is the width of your palm.

How many palms long is:

a telephone book? _____

your desk? _____

a ruler? _____

A "span" is the length from the tip of your pinkie to the tip of your thumb when your hand is wide open.

How many spans long is:

a broom handle? _____

a table? _____

a door? _____

Penguin Family on Parade

The penguin family is part of the winter parade. They need to line up from shortest to tallest. Give them a hand! Use a ruler to measure each penguin. Label each penguin with its height. Then write the name of each penguin in size order, from smallest to tallest.

Paul
Height:

_____

centimetres

Peter
Height:

_____

centimetres

Patty
Height:

_____

centimetres

Petunia
Height:

_____

centimetres

Size Order:

_____   _____   _____   _____

(smallest)   **(tallest)**

Look and Learn

Look at each picture. Estimate how long you think it is. Then measure each picture with a ruler. Write the actual length in centimetres.

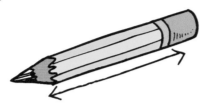

Estimate: _____ centimetres
Actual: _____ centimetres

Estimate: _____ centimetres
Actual: _____ centimetres

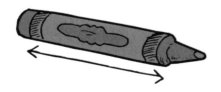

Estimate: _____ centimetres
Actual: _____ centimetres

Estimate: _____ centimetres
Actual: _____ centimetres

Practise measuring other things in the room with a ruler.

Turn Up the Volume

How many litres equal 1 gallon? Find out! Fill a litre container with water. Pour it into a gallon container. Keep doing it until the gallon is full. Colour the correct number of litres below. Write the numeral on the line: **1 gallon = _____ litres.**

Now try it with other containers, too.

1 litre = _____ 250 ml containers

1 250 ml container = _____ cups

1 cup = _____ tablespoons

1 tablespoon = _____ teaspoons

Adding Sides

Use the centimetres on a ruler to measure each side of each rectangle. Write the centimetres in the spaces below. Then add up all the sides to find the perimeter, or distance, around each rectangle.

___ + ___ + ___ + ___ = ____ centimetres

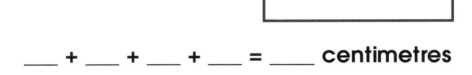

___ + ___ + ___ + ___ = ____ centimetres

___ + ___ + ___ + ___ = ____ centimetres

Centimetres

With a ruler that measures in centimetres, measure the pictures of the objects below.

book

Out Came The Sun

_____ centimetres

book

By The River

_____ centimetres

straw

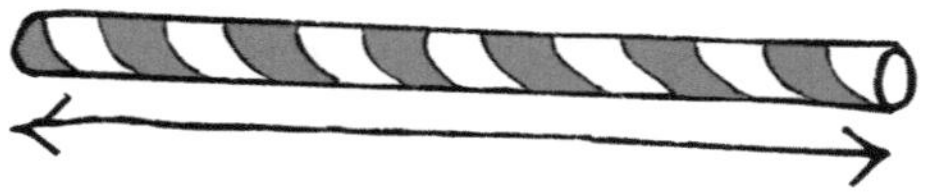

_____ centimetres

marker

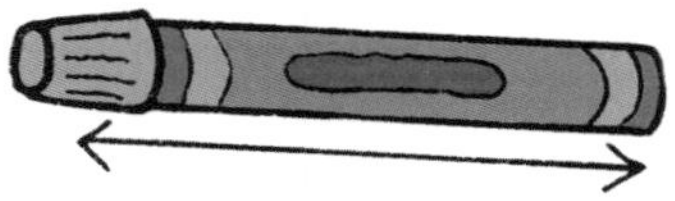

_____ centimetres

5 cubes

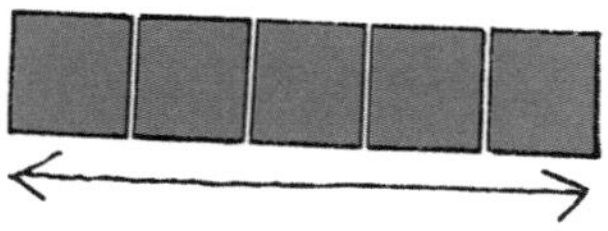

_____ centimetres

10 cubes

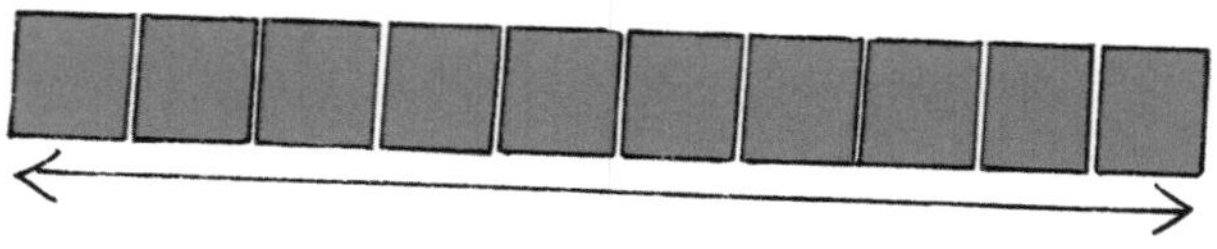

_____ centimetres

shoe

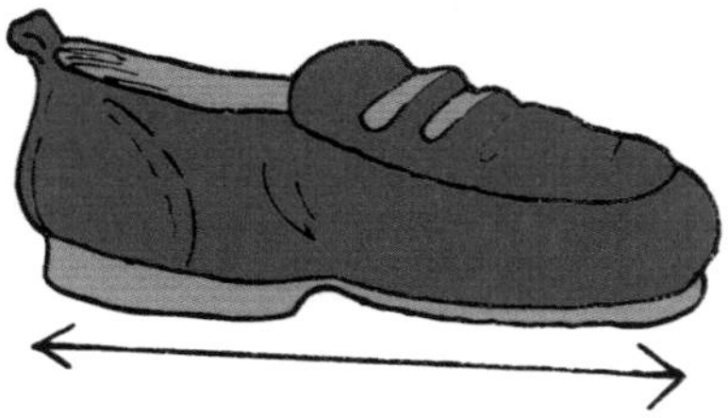

_____ centimetres

hand

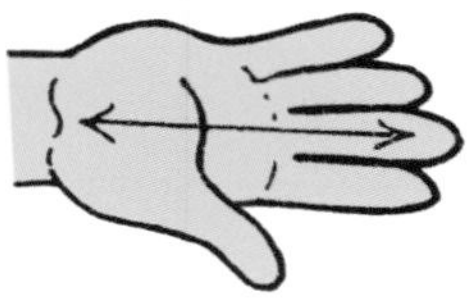

_____ centimetres

Five Senses

We learn about the world by using our 5 senses. The 5 senses are seeing, hearing, smelling, touching, and tasting.
Look at the pictures on the left side of the graph. Think about which of your senses you use to learn about it. Draw a checkmark in the box to show the senses used. (Hint: You might use more than one.)

	See	Hear	Smell	Touch	Taste
🐓					
☀					
🥤					
🌼					
🥁					

Now graph how many senses you used for each object.

5					
4					
3					
2					
1					
	🐓	☀	🥤	🌼	🥁

Rainbow Graph

Which colour of the rainbow is your favourite? Colour in the box for your favourite colour. Have 5 classmates colour the boxes to show their favourite colours, too.

Which colour is liked the most? _____

Which colour is liked the least? _____

Are any colours tied? _____

Which ones? _____

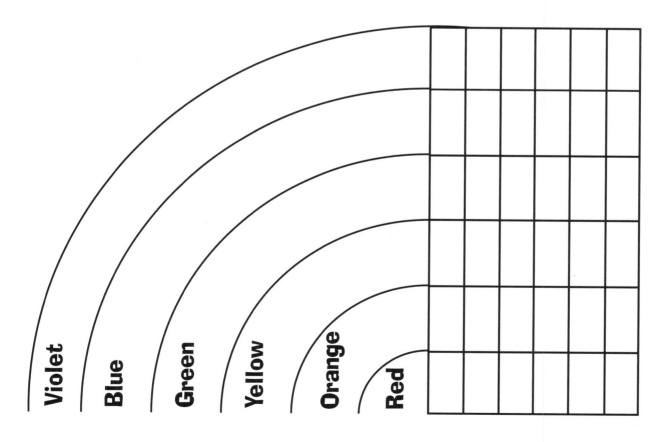

School Supplies

1. Find each letter and
   number pair on the graph.

2. Colour a yellow square
   for each pair.

3. What picture did you make?

   _____

	Across	Up
1.	C	4
2.	C	5
3.	D	4
4.	D	5
5.	E	4
6.	E	5
7.	F	4

	Across	Up
8.	F	5
9.	G	4
10.	G	5
11.	H	4
12.	H	5
13.	I	4
14.	I	5

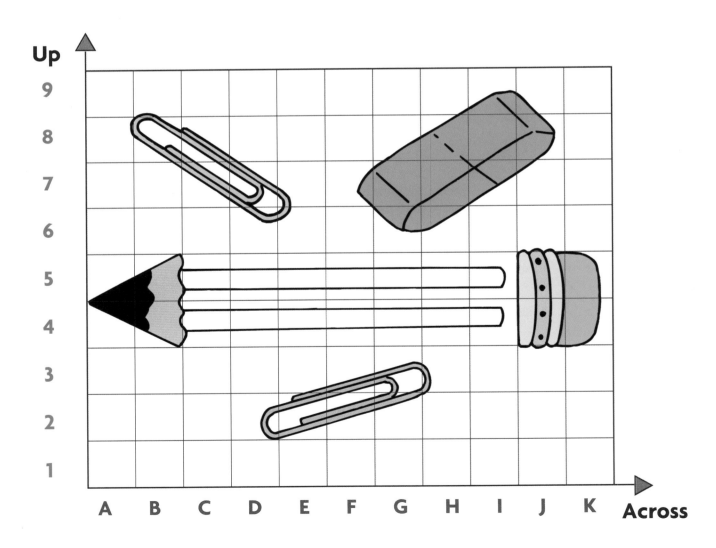

Surprises!

1. Find each number pair on the graph. Make a dot for each.

2. Connect the dots in the order that you make them.

3. What picture did you make?

_____

	Across	Up
1.	9	2
2.	7	4
3.	8	4
4.	6	6
5.	7	6
6.	5	8
7.	3	6
8.	4	6
9.	2	4
10.	3	4
11.	1	2

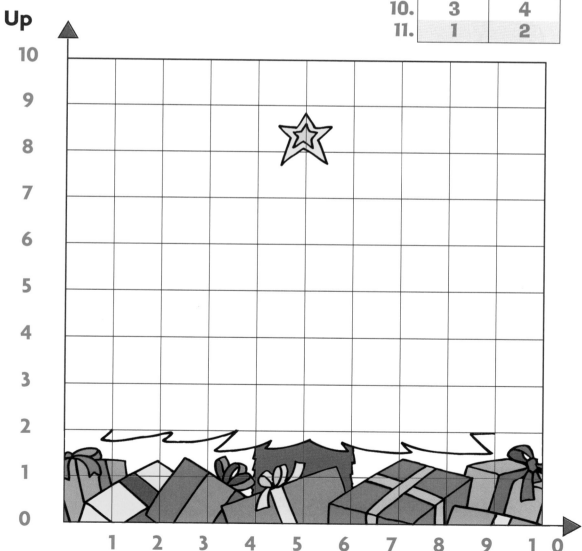

December Weather

In December, Mrs. Monroe's class drew the weather on a calendar. Each kind of weather has a picture:

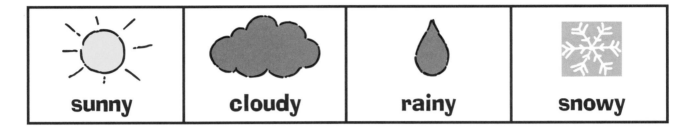

| sunny | cloudy | rainy | snowy |

Look at the calendar. Answer the questions below.

How many sunny days did they have? _____

How many cloudy days did they have? _____

How many rainy days did they have? _____

How many snowy days did they have? _____

Which kind of weather did they have the most? _____

Fun With Fractions

A fraction is a part of a whole.

The shapes below are split into parts, or fractions.
Colour only the shapes that are split into equal parts (equal fractions).

Parts to Colour

 A fraction has two numbers. The top number will tell you how many parts to colour. The bottom number tells you how many parts there are.

Colour 1/5 of the circle.

Colour 4/5 of the rectangle.

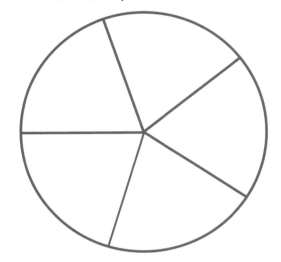

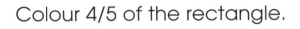

Colour 3/5 of the ants.

Colour 2/5 of the spiders.

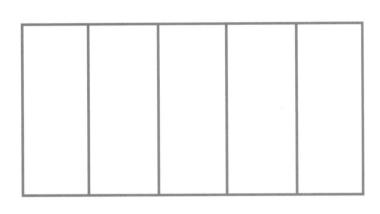

Colour 0/5 of the bees.

Colour 5/5 of the worms.

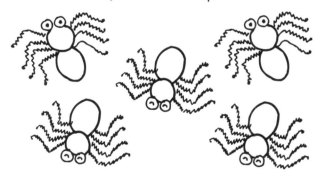

More Parts to Colour

 A fraction has two numbers. The top number will tell you how many parts to colour. The bottom number tells you how many parts there are.

Colour 1/8 of the circle.

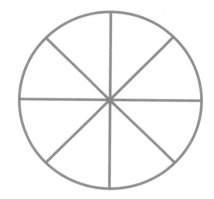

Colour 6/8 of the rectangle.

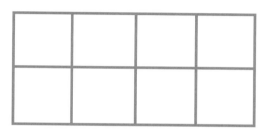

Colour 4/8 of the suns.

Colour 8/8 of the stars.

Colour 2/8 of the moons.

Colour 3/8 of the planets.

Clock Work

Draw the hands on the clock so it shows 2:00.

Draw the hands on the clock so it shows 3:00.

Draw the hands on the clock so it shows 4:00.

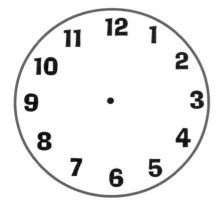

Draw the hands on the clock so it shows 5:00.

What do you do at 2:00 in the afternoon?

Write about it on the lines below.

_____

_____

More Clock Work

Draw the hands on the clock so it shows 3:00.

Draw the hands on the clock so it shows 6:00.

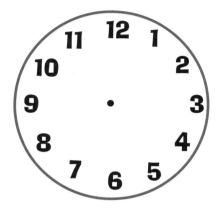

Draw the hands on the clock so it shows 9:00.

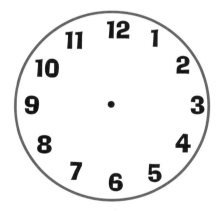

Draw the hands on the clock so it shows 12:00.

What do you do at 3:00 in the afternoon?

Write about it on the lines below.

_____

_____

Even More Clock Work

Draw the hands on the clock so it shows 4:00.

Draw the hands on the clock so it shows 4:30.

What do you do at 4:00 in the afternoon?

Write about it on the line below.

_____

Draw the hands on the clock so it shows 6:00.

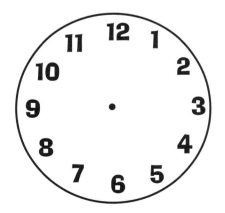

Draw the hands on the clock so it shows 6:30.

What do you do at 6:00 in the evening?

Write about it on the line below.

_____

About Time

Why do we need to know how to tell time? List your ideas below.

_____

_____

_____

_____

How Long Is a Minute?

Think about how much you can do in one minute.
Write your estimates in the Prediction column. Then time yourself.
Write the actual number in the Result column.

Prediction: In One Minute I Can	**Result**
Jump rope _____ times.	
Write the numbers 1 to _____ .	
Say the names of _____ animals.	

Answer Key

READING COMPREHENSION

Page 12
1. a good reader; 2. looks at the picture; 3. the title; 4. the words

Page 13
Main idea: Trucks do important work.

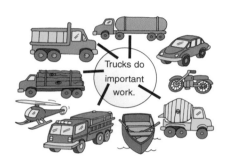

Page 14
Main idea: Clowns can do funny tricks.

Page 15
KATE: Names have special meanings.

Casey means brave.
George means farmer.
Sarah means princess.

Page 16

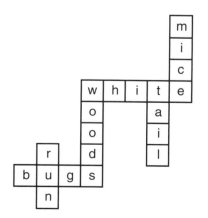

Page 17

1. in reading class; 2. camping

Page 18
Kelly packed pajamas, shirt, shorts, toothbrush, toothpaste, hairbrush, swimsuit, pillow, storybooks, sunglasses. Compound words: grandmother, suitcase, toothbrush, toothpaste, hairbrush, swimsuit, storybooks, sunglasses

Page 19
Make-believe: ketchup bottles and a watermelon bowling, a talking milk jug, dancing bananas, chicken wings that can fly all by themselves, laughing soup cans, dancing carrots

Page 20
Facts: Clouds float in the sky. Clouds are made of tiny drops of water. Fog is a cloud on the ground. (All others are make-believe.)

Page 21
Make-believe: pig, goat and sheep, horses, pizza and hamburgers, mouse and table, golden eggs, crickets (The others are real.)

Page 22
5, 1; 4, 3, 2
Tara bought pencils, scissors, glue, and crayons.

Page 23
6, 4, 2; 3, 1, 5
LEARN TO DIVE

Page 24
1. Each star should be outlined in blue and coloured red inside. 2. One moon should be yellow and one orange. 3. A face should be drawn on each sun. 4. 3; 5. 2; 6. 4; 7. 3 + 2 + 4 = 9; 8. stars moon

Page 25

1.

2.

3.

4.

5.

6.

Page 26

The pictures that do not belong are bike, telephone, snowman, pumpkin, skates, and frog. (The other pictures should be coloured.)

2. hot, cold; 3. up, down; 4. starfish; 5. yellow

Page 27

IT WAS A FLYING CARPET. No

Page 28

1. true; 2. false; 3. false; 4. true; 5. true

Page 29

The children's pictures should include everything described in the sentences.

Page 30

The children should have added these things to the picture: black clouds, lightning striking the tallest tree, the word "Moo" in a bubble above a cow, rain, a mud puddle by the barn door, hay blowing out of the barn window.

Page 31

1. penguin; 2. baby; 3. octopus; 4. ant; 5. grandmother; 6. bear; 7. firefighter

Page 32

1. chicken pox; 2. James scratched them. 3. 9; 4. She got chicken pox, too.

Page 33

Page 34

Bacon and eggs do not belong.

Page 35

Sandie's Shoe Store: sandals, boots, sneakers, high heels; Movie Town Cinema: tickets, popcorn, big screen, candy; Pepe's Mexican Food: tacos, burrito, beans, peppers; Gale's Gardening Goodies: tulip bulbs, fertilizer, gardening gloves, pots

Page 36

Meats: ham, chicken, roast; Dairy: milk, cheese, yogurt; Bread: rolls, bagels, biscuits; Fruits and Vegetables: carrots, corn, apples

Page 37

Page 38

He knew he had to do the right thing.

Page 39

FAST FOOD, FLOWER BED

Page 40

They are in Grade 1.

Page 41
1. Juan's dad; 2. Juan's dad;
3. both; 4. Ann's dad; 5. both;
6. Ann's dad; 7. Juan's dad; 8. both;
9. Ann's dad; 10. both

Page 42
1.

2.

3.

Page 43
1. an arm like a paddle; 2. not dangerous; 3. slap at; 4. lose;
5. hide in the ground

Page 44
1. a small city; 2. little furry animals;
3. tunnels; 4. rooms; 5. pests

Page 45
1. Sandy used lanterns at night because the cabin had no electricity.
2. Sandy and Austin bathed in a stream because the cabin had no running water. 3. Sandy felt better about missing Kendra because she talked to her on the cell phone. 4. Sandy's dad could not call his office because the cell phone was dead.

Page 46
1. The worms got tangled up when they danced. 2. They were tied in a knot so they got married.

Page 47
1. E; 2. B; 3. D; 4. F; 5. A; 6. C.

Page 48
The children's pictures should show a crown on Margie's arm, a shoe on her head, different colours on each fingernail, a red nose, a fork in her hair, and a purple belt around her knees.

6. the way she dresses; 7. He wears his clothes backward.

Page 49
1. happy; 2. worried; 3. silly; 4. sad;
5. scared; 6. surprised

Page 50
1. green; 2. red; 3. red; 4. yellow;
5. red; 6. yellow; 7. green

Page 51
Picture: rainbow 1. appear; 2. gold;
Picture: airplane 3. high; 4. again;
5. bee

Page 52
2. Don't be greedy. Be happy with what you have. Picture answers: dog, meat, bridge

Page 53
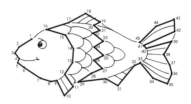

1. sharing 2. Marcus Pfister

TESTS: READING
Pages 57-60

TEST 1
A. Phonic Analysis: Consonants and Vowels
Sample: sun

1. bed   2. cat   3. dog
4. rug   5. sock

B. Vocabulary: Picture-Word Match
Sample: can

1. pig   2. run   3. car

C. High-Frequency Word Match
Sample: and

1. my   2. will   3. sad

D. Grammar, Usage, and Mechanic's
Sample: My bike is red.

1. I like to run.

2. Did you see it?

3. They sit on the mat.

E. Reading Sentences

Sample: A girl sits.

1. The cat plays.
2. The book is on the desk.
3. She has a rabbit.
4. The dog sits on a hill.

F. Story Comprehension

1. dog
2. Rags the Dog
3. play

Pages 61-64

Test 2

A. Phonic Analysis:
Consonants

Sample: bat

1. pot   2. fox   3. bell
4. bus   5. bug

B. Phonic Analysis: Vowels

Sample: cap

1. mop   2. pig   3. sun
4. duck   5. ten

C. High-Frequency
Word Match

Sample: and

1. it   2. she   3. was
4. that   5. they

D. Vocabulary: Picture-Word
Match

Sample: hat

1. bag   2. top   3. pen
4. fan   5. sock

E. Grammar, Usage,
and Mechanics

Sample: The boy is happy.

1. She saw a duck.
2. Look at him run!
3. Where will I go?

F. Story Comprehension

1. a pig
2. Ted's Pig
3. Answers will vary.

Pages 65-68

Test 3

A. Phonic Analysis:
Consonants

Sample: sun

1. ball   2. rug   3. flag
4. pen   5. truck

B. Phonic Analysis: Vowels

Sample: fish

1. bus   2. hat   3. frog
4. nest   5. cake

C. High-Frequency
Word Match

Sample: is

1. for   2. he   3. you
4. said   5. them

D. Vocabulary:
Picture-Word Match

Sample: bird

1. bat   2. dog   3. feet
4. hand   5. clock

E. Grammar, Usage,
and Mechanics

Sample: The girl can jump.

1. The boy ran fast.
2. Look at me!
3. Where will I walk?

F. Story Comprehension

1. a kite
2. Kim's Kite
3. Answers will vary.

Pages 69-72

Test 4

A. Phonic Analysis:
Consonants

Sample: dog

1. bat   2. fan   3. tree
4. moon   5. fish

B. Phonic Analysis: Vowels

Sample: sun

1. map   2. web   3. fox
4. pig   5. cake

C. High-Frequency
Word Match

Sample: and

1. for   2. she   3. how
4. can   5. then

D. Vocabulary:
Picture-Word Match

Sample: pen

1. hat   2. frog   3. bus
4. feet   5. bike

E. Grammar, Usage,
and Mechanics

Sample: The

1. She
2. They
3. out!
4. day?
5. Amy.
6. I
7. We
8. his
9. Anna and Tim

F. Story Comprehension
1. a cat
2. string
3. Nate's Cat
4. Answers will vary

.

Pages 73-76

Test 5

A. Phonic Analysis: Consonants
Sample: baby
1. sheep   2. bath   3. snail
4. tree   5. frog

B. Phonic Analysis: Vowels
Sample: car
1. spoon   2. legs
3. puppies   4. boy   5. milk

C. High-Frequency Word Match
Sample: is
1. to   2. said   3. hello
4. best   5. smell

D. Vocabulary:
   Picture-Word Match
Sample: ant
1. wet   2. dish   3. saw
4. bug   5. cake

E. Grammar, Usage,
   and Mechanics
Sample: is
1. I
2. The
3. me!
4. Nan and Nell
5. you
6. We
7. They
8. Joey.
9. She

F. Story Comprehension
1. goldfish
2. Goldie and Finny
3. bowl

Pages 77-80

Test 6

A. Phonic Analysis: Consonants
Sample: bag
1. mop   2. cheese   3. ten
4. fish   5. train

B. Phonic Analysis: Vowels
Sample: sun
1. six   2. cat   3. boat
4. teeth   5. foot

C. High-Frequency
   Word Match
Sample: me
1. is   2. said   3. where

D. Grammar, Usage, and
   Mechanics
Sample: The dog is furry.
1. He didn't like it.
2. Can you run fast?
3. Where can I play?

E. Reading Sentences
Sample: A boy runs.
1. She put the sock in the box.
2. The nest has ten eggs.
3. She plays on the swing.
4. The truck can go fast.

F. Story Comprehension
1. read
2. Books Tom Reads
3. animals
4. Pet Rabbits

Pages 81-84

Test 7

A. Phonic Analysis: Consonants
Sample: fish
1. pen   2. broom   3. nest
4. truck   5.cheese

B. Phonic Analysis: Vowels
Sample: bat
1. ten   2. house   3. leaf
4. book   5. plane

C. High-Frequency
   Word Match
Sample: and
1. has   2. come   3. what

D. Grammar, Usage,
   and Mechanics
Sample: The cat sleeps.
1. Why can't we go?
2. They play all day.
3. Can Sam sit with us?

E. Reading Sentences
Sample: The boy kicks the ball.
1. The duck swims in the pond.
2. She rides her bike.
3. The leaf fell off the branch.
4. He can see the cow.

F. Story Comprehension
1. The Wind.
2. to fly a kite
3. seeds grow
4. blow away a leaf

Pages 85-88

Test 8

A. Phonic Analysis: Consonants
Sample: desk
1. pan   2. tree   3. ship
4. clock   5. hand

B. Phonic Analysis
Sample: net
1. cup   2. moon   3. cloud
4. boat   5. rake

**C. Vocabulary:
  Picture-Word Match**
Sample: fish
1. bed   2. nest   3. plane
4. coat   5. kite

D. High-Frequency Word Match
Sample: in
1. him   2. then   3. says
4. our   5. what

**E. Grammar, Usage and
  Mechanics**
Sample: He rides in a plane.
1. She runs very fast.
2. Where are my socks?
3. We play with the dog.

F. Story Comprehension
1. Rabbits
2. hear sounds from far away
3. in holes in the ground and in
   people's homes
4. Answers will vary.

Pages 89-92

Test 9

A. Phonic Analysis: Consonants
Sample: dress
1. train   2. flag   3. lamp
4. desk   5. spoon

B. Phonic Analysis: Vowels
Sample: fox
1. bell   2. gate   3. hose
4. teeth   5. leaf

C. High-Frequency Word Match
Sample: her
1. very   2. some   3. there
4. which   5. because

**D. Vocabulary:
  Picture-Word Match**
Sample: frog
1. kite   2. fish   3. plane
4. cupcake   5. butterfly

**E. Grammar, Usage,
  and Mechanics**
Sample: We
1. jump.   2. Dr. Jones   3. I
4. New Brunswick   5. rides

F. Story Comprehension
1. Jane Goodall
2. Africa
3. 3 years old
4. Answers will vary

.

Pages 93-96

Test 10

A. Phonic Analysis: Consonants
Sample: dog
1. six   2. tree   3. top
4. fan   5. ship

B. Phonic Analysis: Vowels
Sample: hat
1. sock   2. sun   3. coat
4. train   5. bike

C. High Frequency Word Match
Sample: the
1. is   2. have   3. said

**D. Grammar, Usage,
  and Mechanics**
Sample: The boy is happy.
1. She can't help us.
2. Can we play ball?
3. Where will I go?

E. Reading Sentences
Sample: A girl runs.
1. He walks the dog.
2. I can sit next to you.
3. The man has a big hat.
4. I like to play games.

F. Story Comprehension
1. dogs and cats
2. Good Pets
3. run and jump

Pages 97-100

Test 11

A. Phonic Analysis: Consonants
Sample: door
1. plant   2. twelve
3. thumb   4. sneakers
5. bench

B. Phonic Analysis: Vowels
Sample: girl
1. mouse   2. game
3. button   4. skates   5. egg

C. High-Frequency Word Match
Sample: send
1. that   2. like   3. sit
4. of   5. book

**D. Vocabulary:
  Picture-Word Match**
Sample: jump
1. brush   2. friends   3. pants
4. bill   5. nine

**E. Grammar, Usage,
  and Mechanics**
Sample: eats
1. My   2. lives   3. is
4. Do   5. have   6. They

F. Story Comprehension
1. Baby Penguins
2. three days
3. the mother and father
4. Answers will vary.

GRAMMAR

Page 148
1. The 2. The 3. The 4. The

Page 149
1. The cat sat. 2. The dog sat.
3. I see the cat. 4. I can see.

Page 150
1. The 2. My 3. Jan 4. I 5. Ants

Page 151
1. I see Jan. 2. I go with Jan.
3. We see Dan.
4. I go with Dan and Jan.
5. school. 6. school.

Page 152
1. Dan is in the cab.
2. The cat is in the cab.
3. Mom is in the cab.
4. We see Dan and Mom.
5. van. 6. red.

Page 153
1. The cat is on the mat.
2. The rat is on the mop.
3. The rat sees the cat.
4. The rat can hop.
5. The cat and rat sit.

Page 154
1. I like to hop.
2. Pam and I like to hop.
3. I can hop to Mom.
4. Mom and I can hop.
5. Answers will vary.

Page 155
1. I 2. I 3. I 4. I 5.
Answers will vary.

Page 156
1. I sit on a mat. 2. Pam and I like cats. 3. I see the van. 4. I like jam.
5. I like to nap.

Page 157
1. Pam 2. Dan 3. The cat
4. The van
5. Jan is hot. ________ 
6. The hat is on top. ___ 
7. The man sat. ________ 

Page 158
1. Bill paints. 2. Tom likes to read.
3. Pat plants flowers.
4. Answers will vary.

Page 159
1. The cat sits on a mat. 2. Pam and Dan like jam. 3. I see Mom. 4. I like my hat. 5. Ben can hop.

Page 160
1. I 2. Pam 3. We 4. We
1. I like dots.
2. Pam likes dots.
3. We like hats.
4. We like hats with dots.

Page 161
1. I like cats. 2. I see a man.
3. We go to school

Page 162
1. I see red dots. 2. Dan is in a big van. 3. The cat is fat. 4. We like the hat. 5. Ben likes jam.

Page 163
1. ? 2. ? 3. ? 4. ?
5. Answers will vary.
6. Answers will vary.

Page 164
1. Who hid the cat?
2. Can the cat see the rat ?
4. Can the van go?
5. Can we sit in the van?
6. Can Dan nap in the van?

Page 165
1. Who hid my hat?
2. Did the hat have dots?
3. Did Jan like my hat?
4. Can you see the hat?
5. Dan has the hat?

Page 166
1. pig 2. pan 3. Pam 4. hill
5. The sun is hot. ______ 
6. Sam ran and ran. _____ 
7. Is the cat fat? ________ 

Page 167
1. Al, van 2. cat, mat 3. Pat, hill
4. Dan, Jan

Page 168
1. c. 2. b 3. b 4. a 5. c

Page 169
1. Hill Park 2. Pam 3. Don
4. Frog Lake 5. Answers will vary.

Page 170
1. Pam 2. Ant Hill 3. Ron
4. Bat Lake 5. Spot 6. Hill Street

Page 171
1. Don 2. Pig Hill 3. Jam Street
4. Jan 5. Ham Lake

Page 172
1. sits 2. ran 3. hid 4. naps 5. run
6. see

Page 173
1. see 2. sits 3. mops 4. run
5. hops

Page 174
1. b 2. a 3. c 4. c 5. a

Page 175
1. big 2. fast 3. bad 4. fat
5. fat 6. little

Page 176
1. little, fast
2. hot, big
3. It is fat.
4. They are little.

Page 177
1. silly 2. bad 3. black 4. big
5. green

Page 178
1. (I), 2. (T), 3. (H), 4. (T),.
5. I can fill the basket.
6. Can you get the mop?
7. We can clean.

Page 179
1. She has a mop. _____
2. The dog is on top. __
3. Dan gets the hats. __
4. Ron can clean spots. __
5. (P)ut it in the pot(.)
6. Is it in the pan?

Page 180
1. You can get it.
2. The basket is big.
3. The hat is in the basket.
4. A cat can not go in it.
5. We can fill the basket.

Page 181
1. Help(!) The rat is on top(!)
2. Get the cat(!)
3. This cat is bad(!)
4. Uh-oh(!) The cat is wet(!)
5. Oh my(!) Get the dog(!)
6. Oh(!) The dog runs(!)

Page 182
1. Run to the show!
2. Oh my, I'm very late!
3. What a great show!
4. Watch out, the floor is wet!
5. Wow, we had lots of fun!

Page 183
1. Yes! The cow can kick!
2. That cat is bad!
3. That rat runs fast!
4. Oh no! A frog is in my house!
5. The pot is hot!

Page 184
1. hats 2. eggs 3. girls 4. cats
5. mugs 6. hands

Page 185
1. Jan has her mittens.
2. She will run up hills.
3. Jan runs with her dogs.
4. The dogs can jump.
5. cats 6. socks

Page 186
1. hands 2. pots 3. dogs 4. ants
5. frogs

Page 187
1. sits 2. sees 3. digs 4. naps
5. sees 6. run

Page 188
1. play 2. dance 3. talk 4. run

Page 189
1. sits 2. naps 3. hops
4. digs 5. ran

Page 190
1. school 2. ball 3. girl 4. friends
Person: girl Place: school
Thing: ball

Page 191
1. Run and kick
   in the park. _____
2. Kick with a foot. __
3. Kick the ball. __
4. The girl will run
   to get it. __
5. Kick it to the net. __

Page 192
1. park 2. girl 3. ball 4. friend
5. net

Page 193
1. The king is sad.
2. Let's bake him a cake.
3. Tell the king to come.
4. Let's eat the cake.
The king eats.

Page 194
1. This bear likes snow.
2. The water is cold.
3. The bear runs fast.
4. Two bears play.

Page 195
1. Pam will bake a cake.
2. Pam will see the king.
3. The king has a duck.
4. The duck is in the lake.
5. The king will eat cake.

Page 196
circle: What, See, Night, The, Light, Moon, See, Many, Stars, The, Sun, Moon

Answers will vary.

Page 197
1. look, stars 2. the, moon, shines, night 3. we, see, planets 4. many, moons, shine 5. night, day 6. The Sun in the Sky 7. See the Stars!

Page 198
1. Where is the Sun? 2. Many Cats to See 3. Day and Night 4. How Many Pigs? 5. The Big, Bad Wolf

Page 199
1. pot 2. pan 3. top 4. Jim
5. The pot is hot. ___
6. See the pan? ____
7. Jim is fast. _____

Page 200
1. Jan, van 2. van 3. van, hill
4. Dan, Jan 5. answers will vary

Page 201
1. pans 2. Jim 3. cat 4. rat 5. cat

Page 202
1. is 2. were 3. was 4. are 5. now
6. in the past 7. now

Page 203
1. are, now 2. is, now 3. was, past
4. is, now 5. were, past

Page 204
1. was 2. were 3. are 4. is 5. are

Page 205
1. The, Gruff 2. They, Troll 3. His, Nosey 4. He 5. Dan and Pam like the play. Names a person, place, or thing. 6. They will read it to Jim.
First word in a sentence.

Page 206
1. Raul 2. Mrs. Chin 3. Sue
4. Lee Park

Page 207
1. I   2. Ron 3. Gruff 4. Troll
5. Nosey

WRITING

Page 210

The	For	That	with	know	but
here	on	When	Have	next	we
as	after	good	Make	there	see
Go	Look	Are	Could	is	why
This	who	said	in	come	them
Has	Name	Before	Her	Where	The

Page 211
1. The mouse; 2. He finds; 3. He eats; 4. Then he; 5. Oh no!;
6. The mouse

Page 212
1. We read; 2. Then we; 3. My bed; 4. My cat; 5. The sky; 6. My eyes

Page 213
1. My dog; 2. She must; 3. Maybe she; 4. Sometimes she; 5. I think

Page 214
Check that the child has added a period to the end of each sentence.

Page 215
Check that the child has added a period to the end of each sentence.

Page 216
1. Frogs and toads lay eggs. 2. The eggs are in the water. 3. Tadpoles hatch from the eggs. 4. The tadpoles grow legs. 5. The tadpoles lose their tails.

Page 217
1. Tadpoles become frogs or toads. 2. Frogs live near water. 3. Toads live under bushes. 4. Frogs have wet skin. 5. Toads have bumpy skin.

Page 218

Page 219
Five boats are sailing.; We have four buckets.

Page 220
A jaguar is hiding.; Some butterflies are blue.; Frogs jump in the water.; Green snakes hang from trees.; The trees grow very tall.

Page 221
The snakes on the left side of the page should have been coloured.

Page 222
1. The blue snake;
2. The yellow snake;
3. The green snake;
4. The brown snake;
5. The red snake; 6. The purple snake; 7. The black snake; 8. The orange snake

Page 223
Sentences will vary.

Page 224
Sentences will vary.

Page 225
Sentences will vary.

Page 226
Sentences will vary.

Page 227
The bones on the right side of the page should have been coloured.

Page 228
1. is jumping.; 2. is barking.; 3. is eating.; 4. is sleeping.

Page 229
Sentences will vary.

Page 230
Answers will vary.

Page 231
Sentences will vary.

Page 232
Sentences will vary.

Page 233
Pictures will vary.

Page 234
Answers will vary.

Page 235
1. long ago; 2. yesterday; 3. in winter;
4. today; 5. in the fall; 6. last night;
7. all day; 8. at noon;
9. yesterday; 10. on Thanksgiving Day; 11. this morning; 12. Tomorrow

Page 236
Sentences will vary.

Page 237
Answers will vary.

Page 238
Sentences will vary.

Page 239
Sentences will vary.

Page 240
Sentences will vary.

Page 241
kitten, bat, cracker, ball

Page 242
sweet, red, smooth; bumpy, salty, crunchy,; small, squeaky, furry

Page 243
Adjectives will vary.

Page 244
Sentences will vary.

Page 245
Sentences will vary.

Page 246
Sentences will vary.

Page 247
Sentences will vary.

Page 248
Sentences will vary.

Page 249
My Space Friend; A Big Beak; The Big Win; A Knight's Tale

Page 250
Stories will vary.

Page 251
Sentences will vary.

Page 252
Sentences and pictures will vary.

MAPS

Page 254
1. yes
2. yes
3. yes
4. no
5. swimming pool; car; lawn

Page 255
Child should colour answers on map.

Page 256
4. truck
5. yes

Page 257
Child should colour answers on map.

Page 259
1. far
2. near
3. above

Pages 260–261
1. yes
2. yes
3. no
4. yes
5. school
6. flower shop
7. Map 3
8. Map 1

Page 262
1. round
2. people, animals, plants
3. Drawings will vary.

Page 263
1. blue, green, orange, yellow, purple, red

2. blue
3. smaller

Page 264
1. south
2. east

Page 265
1. east
2. north
3. west
4. south

Page 266
1. north
2. east
3. north
4. west

Page 267
1–4 Line begins at gate, runs north to popcorn, west to Ferris wheel, east to face painting, west to popcorn and north to arcade.
5. south

Page 268
1. c.
2. a.
3. d.
4. b.

Page 269
1. tree
2. airplane
3. railroad track
4. beach umbrella

Page 270
1. garden
2. road
3. house
4. stable

Page 271
1. south
2. sheep
3. west
4. Tree symbol should be drawn for forest.

Pages 272–273
1. mountain
2. plain
3. hill
4. river
5. mountain
6. hill
7. lake

Page 274
1–4 Child should write answers on picture.

Page 275
1. plain
2. east
3. west
4. Answers will vary.

Page 276
1. hill
2. campground
3. picnic table
4. river or lake
5. west

Page 277
1. Doony Park
2. snack stand
3. a fountain
4. dog run
5. playground
6. west

Page 278

1. school
2. apartment
3. store
4. house
5. Drawings will vary.

Page 279

1. school
2. Spring Street
3. Summer Street
4. west

Page 280

1. South Street
2. West Street
3. North Street
4. South Street

Page 281

1. Routes will vary.
2. East Street
4. west
5. north

Page 283

1. border
2. road
3. a river
4. south
5. west

Page 284

1. country border
2. United States
3. south

Page 285

1. Atlantic Ocean
2. Pacific Ocean

Pages 286–287

2. Atlantic, Pacific, Arctic, Indian, Southern
3. Europe
4. South America
5. Indian Ocean
6. Arctic Ocean
7. Antarctica

Page 288

1. lake
2. hill
3. North Street
4. Routes will vary.
5. post office on South Street
6. north

Page 289

1. south
2. lake
3. border
4. symbol
5. mountain
6. route
7. ocean

ADDITION & SUBTRACTION

Page 294

Check child's colouring.

Page 295

1 + 2 = 3, 2 + 3 = 5, 7 + 3 = 10; 3 + 4 = 7, 1 + 0 = 1, 3 + 2 = 5; 1 + 1 = 2, 4 + 4 = 8; 1 + 3 = 4; The ladybug with 10 spots should be coloured red. The ladybug with 1 spot should be coloured blue.

Page 296

Check that the child has drawn the correct number of flowers. 7: needs 3, 10: needs 5, 4: needs 1; 6: needs 2, 9: needs 5, 5: needs 3, 8: needs 4, 3: needs 2; Colour the bows with the numbers 4, 6, 8, and 10 yellow. Colour the bows with 3, 5, 7, and 9 purple.

Page 297

A SAXOPHONE

6 + 2 = 8; 5 + 1 = 6; 4 + 4 = 8

3 + 6 = 9; 3 + 0 = 3; 3 + 4 = 7

2 + 2 = 4; 2 + 1 = 3; 1 + 1 = 2

0 + 1 = 1

Page 298

5 − 3 = 2; 7 − 4 = 3; 10 − 5 = 5; 9 − 2 = 7; 8 − 7 = 1; 9 − 6 = 3; 6 − 1 = 5; 10 − 2 = 8; 7 − 5 = 2; 5 − 1 = 4; 8 − 2 = 6; 8 − 0 = 8; 9 − 7 = 2; 8 − 5 = 3; 10 − 4 = 6; 10 − 3 = 7; 9 − 4 = 5; 8 − 1 = 7; 6 − 4 = 2; 6 − 3 = 3; 7 − 2 = 5; 9 − 0 = 9; 10 − 1 = 9

Page 299

2, 3, 2; 3, 2, 1

Pages 300–301

1. 9 − 4 = 5; 2. 8 − 1 = 7;
3. 10 − 3 = 7; 4. 8 − 6 = 2;
5. 7 − 2 = 5; 6. 8 − 4 = 4
7. 10 − 4 = 6; 8. 8 − 2 = 6;
9. 9 − 6 = 3

Page 302

Page 303

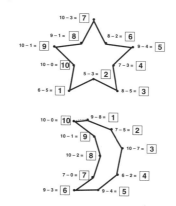

Page 304

4, 3, 2; 10, 1, 7; 6, 8, 5; The rabbit moved right to add. The rabbit moved left to subtract.

Page 305

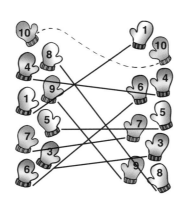

Page 306

IT'S OUT OF THIS WORLD!

Page 307

A. 6 + 2 = 8; B. 3 + 1 = 4;
C. 6 − 4 = 2

Page 308

A. 6 + 4 = 10; B. 10 − 5 = 5; C. 9 − 2 = 7; D. 4 + 6 = 10; E. 7 + 2 = 9; F. 2 + 3 = 5; G. 5 + 3 = 8; H. 6 + 4 = 10; I. 8 − 7 = 1; J. 10 − 3 = 7

Page 309

A. 7 + 3 = 10; B. 7 − 4 = 3; C. 10 − 6 = 4; D. 8 − 2 = 6; E. 5 + 4 = 9

Page 310

Check child's colouring.
11 ways; 0 + 10 = 10, 1 + 9 = 10, 2 + 8 = 10, 3 + 7 = 10, 4 + 6 = 10, 5 + 5 = 10, 6 + 4 = 10, 7 + 3 = 10, 8 + 2 = 10, 9 + 1 = 10, 0 + 10 = 10

Page 311

7 leaps

Page 312

8 + 7 = 15; 3 + 7 = 10; 8 + 6 = 14;
9 + 9 = 18; 1 + 1 = 2; 5 + 2 = 7;
3 + 2 = 5; 9 + 2 = 11; 4 + 2 = 6;
1 + 4 = 5; 2 + 2 = 4; 7 + 4 = 11;
5 + 8 = 13; 6 + 2 = 8; 7 + 7 = 14;
5 + 5 = 10; 4 + 7 = 11; 3 + 3 = 6;
1 + 7 = 8; 3 + 8 = 11; 5 + 0 = 5;
9 + 6 = 15; 5 + 3 = 8; 2 + 5 = 7;
0 + 2 = 2; 3 + 1 = 4; 9 + 7 = 16;
7 + 5 = 12; 6 + 1 = 7; 9 + 8 = 17;
1 + 5 = 6; 6 + 6 = 12

Page 313

Beans talk.

4 + 2 = 6; 7 + 7 = 14; 9 + 5 = 14

10 + 4 = 14; 4 + 8 = 12; 6 + 8 = 14

11 + 3 = 14; 14 + 0 = 14; 7 + 2 = 9

13 + 1 = 14; 5 + 8 = 13; 12 + 2 = 14

7 + 4 = 11; 5 + 9 = 14

Page 314

A.
2	4	6
3	1	4
5	5	10

B.
4	1	5
7	3	10
11	4	15

C.
6	7	13
2	1	3
8	8	16

D.
5	6	11
4	3	7
9	9	18

E.
2	6	8
5	0	5
7	6	13

F.
4	7	11
3	3	6
7	10	17

Page 315

8, 8; 4, 4; 6, 6; 8, 8; 1, 1; 3, 3; 9, 9; 2, 2; 5, 5; 7, 7; even

Page 316

7 + 7 = 14, 5 + 5 = 10, 8 + 8 = 16, 6 + 6 = 12; 9 + 9 = 18, 3 + 3 = 6, 2 + 2 = 4; 4 + 4 = 8

Page 317

A. 4; B. 6; C. 10; D. 9;
E. 7; F. 2; G. 5; H. 8; I. 3; J. 1; K. 5 − 2 = 3; L. 9 − 3 = 6; M. 7 − 5 = 2; N. 8 − 1 = 7; O. 12 − 6 = 6; P. 16 − 8 = 8; Q. 14 − 5 = 9

Page 318

four, five; seven, eleven; nine, six; ten, three; eight, two

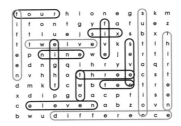

Page 319

7 + 2 = **9** − 4 = **5** − 3 = **2** + 9 = **11** + 5 = **16** − 8 = **8** + 4 = **12** + 6 = **18** − 9 = **9** + 1 = **10** + 4 = **14** − 8 = **6** + 2 = **8** + 3 = **11** − 3 = **8**; 12 − 3 = **9** − 6 = **3** + 2 = **5** + 9 = **14** − 6 = **8** + 7 = **15** − 6 = **9** + 3 = **12** − 2 = **10** + 7 = **17** + 1 = **18** − 11 = **7** − 5 = **2** + 13 = **15** − 7 = **8** + 3 = **11**; Colour the bottom car blue.

Page 320

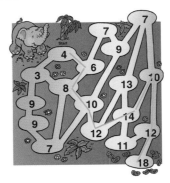

3 peanuts

Page 321

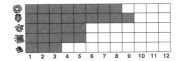

3, 3; 7, 7; 9, 9; 5, 5; 8, 8

Page 322

A. First flower should be circled.;
B. 8 + 9 = 17; C. 5 − 5 = 0;
D. 5 + 3 = 8; E. 5 − 3 = 2;
F. 9 + 5 = 14

Page 323

A. 13, 12, 13, 13; B. 12, 11, 11, 11;
C. 17, 15, 15, 17; D. 14, 14, 14, 16
Check child's colouring.

Page 324

- 1; 12, 11, 10, 9, 8, 7
+2; 2, 4, 6, 8, 10, 12
+3; 3, 6, 9, 12, 15, 18
-2; 13, 11, 9, 7, 5, 3

Page 325

2, 4, 2; 3, 5, 4; 6, 4, 10;
Answers will vary.

Page 326

5; 3 + 2 + 5 = 10; 4 + 5 + 7 = 16; 6; 7
+ 2 = 9; 6 − 2 = 4; 7 + 4 + 5 + 3 + 2
= 21; 1 + 7 + 6 + 3 + 2 = 19

Page 327

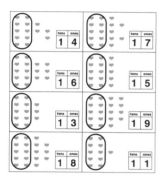

Page 328

Check child's colouring.; 14 days

Page 329

	17	36	84	
78	29	59	14	48
88	24	35	66	98
18	43	77	38	88
78	65	56	46	26
	99	57	87	

Page 330

93 + 6 = 99, 82 + 4 = 86, 14 + 5 =
19, 21 + 7 = 28, 53 + 6 = 59; 45 + 4
= 49, 73 + 3 = 76, 36 + 3 = 39, 61 +
5 = 66, 32 + 7 = 39; 4 + 7 + 5 + 3 +
6 = 25

Page 331

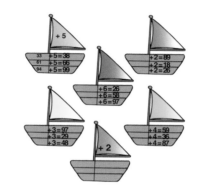

Page 332

Check child's colouring.

Page 333

A. 39 − 7 = 32; B. 54 − 1 = 53; C. 87
− 6 = 81;
D. 73 − 3 = 70; E. 25 − 4 = 21; F. 42
− 2 = 40;
G. 98 − 7 = 91; H. 66 − 5 = 61;
4, 7, 5

Page 334

42, 90, 76, 32, 82, 63, 81; 50, 35,
21, 21, 41, 90, 53; 30, 80, 20, 70,
60, 65, 74; The box with 53 should
be coloured yellow. The box with 32
should be coloured orange. The box
with 74 should be coloured red.

Page 335

Check child's colouring.

Page 336

AT

12 + 13 = 25; 24 + 34 = 58;
22 + 21 = 43; 77 + 22 = 99;
35 + 43 = 78; 52 + 12 = 64
40 + 52 = 92; 11 + 31 = 42;
30 + 39 = 69; 46 + 52 = 98;
15 + 12 = 27; 10 + 71 = 81;
63 + 11 = 74; 13 + 80 = 93;
36 + 32 = 68; 30 + 10 = 40;
11 + 11 = 22; 15 + 4 = 19
20 + 21 = 41; 15 + 11 = 26;
22 + 33 = 55; 14 + 14 = 28;
13 + 16 = 29; 10 + 20 = 30;
14 + 25 = 39; 11 + 20 = 31;
15 + 21 = 36; 20 + 31 = 51;
36 + 52 = 88; 21 + 32 = 53;
10 + 50 = 60; 44 + 41 = 85;
24 + 43 = 67; 31 + 21 = 52;
13 + 82 = 95;

Page 337

32 + 24 = 56; 16 + 40 = 56;
54 + 14 = 68; 77 + 12 = 89;
34 + 34 = 68; 53 + 36 = 89;
26 + 63 = 89; 23 + 45 = 68;
35 + 62 = 97; 38 + 30 = 68;
22 + 67 = 89; 47 + 42 = 89

Page 338

HE WAS A CHICKEN.

13 + 11 = 24; 26 + 33 = 59;
16 + 31 = 47; 10 + 12 = 22;
64 + 24 = 88; 20 + 15 = 35;
71 + 12 = 83; 25 + 21 = 46;
51 + 10 = 61; 22 + 16 = 38;
22 + 10 = 32; 14 + 14 = 28;
20 + 10 = 30; 25 + 31 = 56;
21 + 3 = 24; 42 + 30 = 72;
13 + 43 = 56; 54 + 15 = 69;
21 + 61 = 82; 61 + 33 = 94;
10 + 30 = 40; 20 + 30 = 50;
16 + 32 = 48; 71 + 23 = 94;
70 + 20 = 90

Page 339

A BAT

5 − 2 = 3; 7 − 7 = 0; 18 − 9 = 9;
17 − 3 = 14; 15 − 4 = 11;
18 − 4 = 14; 12 − 3 = 9;
11 − 9 = 2; 16 − 9 = 7; 7 − 4 = 3;
10 − 8 = 2; 15 − 7 = 8; 9 − 2 = 7;
13 − 2 = 11; 12 − 2 = 10;
15 − 2 = 13; 9 − 6 = 3; 6 − 6 = 0;
9 − 7 = 2; 15 − 9 = 6; 16 − 8 = 8;
9 − 5 = 4; 9 − 1 = 8

Page 340

77 − 30 = 47; 76 − 62 = 14;
59 − 12 = 47; 85 − 52 = 33;
98 − 84 = 14; 87 − 40 = 47;
98 − 35 = 63; 58 − 11 = 47;
88 − 62 = 26; 77 − 14 = 63;
69 − 22 = 47; 38 − 12 = 26;
75 − 12 = 63; 97 − 71 = 26;
97 − 50 = 47; 98 − 51 = 47;
43 − 10 = 33; 87 − 73 = 14;
78 − 31 = 47; 97 − 64 = 33;
99 − 52 = 47

Page 341

1. 7 − 1 = 6; 2. 9 − 2 = 7;
3. 3 − 2 = 1; 4. 8 − 4 = 4,
5. 5 − 5 = 0; 6. 6 − 1 = 5;
7. 8 − 2 = 6
The phone number is 671-4056.

Page 342

27, 74, 41, 65; 27, 70, 42, 53; 15, 23,
11, 33; 20, 2, 15, 31; 22

Page 343

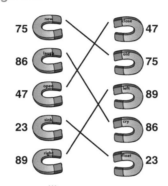

Answers will vary.

Page 344

34 + 13 = 47, 21 + 52 = 73, 47 + 10
= 57; 75 − 34 = 41, 62 − 21 = 41, 47
− 13 = 34

Page 345

A. Sunday; B. 89;
C. Monday; D. 24; E. 79; F. 22;
Sunday, Tuesday, Saturday

Page 346

34, 85, 26, 57; star; 71, 88, 42, 76,
85; light; 76, 63, 26, 85; heat; 71, 88,
13, 63; life

Page 347

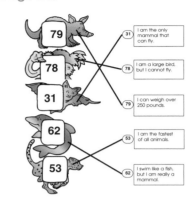

Page 348

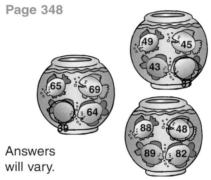

Answers will vary.

MATH

Page 351

Check child's picture to make sure
each shape has the correct colour:

6 = yellow;

7 = green;

8 = brown;

9 = red;

10 = green.

Page 352

Answers will vary, but check to make
sure that child has supplied correct
numbers for each category.

Page 353

Check to make sure that child has
drawn lines from five different frogs
to the lily pads.

Extra: 2

Page 354

1. Answers will vary.

2. Numbers will be coloured in using an AB pattern of red and blue.

Page 355

Possible groups

Balls: soccer ball, basketball, rubber ball

Winter clothes: scarf, hat, boots

Art supplies: paint, paintbrush, crayon

Page 356

Check child's picture to make sure that each shape has the correct colour:

one = green;

two = yellow;

three = red;

four = purple;

five = blue.

Page 357

Yield sign: triangle, 3

Caution sign: diamond, 4

Speed-limit sign: rectangle, 4

Stop sign: octagon, 8

Page 358

Left birdhouse: cube, octagon, hexagon, rectangle, square, rectangle solid

Right birdhouse: cylinder, triangle, circle, rectangle

Page 359

Colour the first butterfly, the second heart, the lightbulb, and the snowflake; drawings should show the other halves.

Page 360

1. 32, 42, 52, 62, 72, 82, 92

2. 70, 60, 50, 40, 30, 20, 10

3. 67, 57, 47, 37, 27, 17, 7

4. 44, 55, 66, 77, 88, 99

Page 361

A salamander

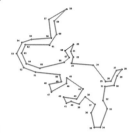

Page 362

Estimates will vary. 2, 4, 6, 8, 10, 12, 14, 16, 18, 20, 5, 10, 15, 20

Extra: No. Snowflakes would melt before you could count them.

Page 363

1	2	3	4	5	6	7	8	9	10
11	12	13	14	15	16	17	18	19	20
21	22	23	24	25	26	27	28	29	30
31	32	33	34	35	36	37	38	39	40
41	42	43	44	45	46	47	48	49	50
51	52	53	54	55	56	57	58	59	60
61	62	63	64	65	66	67	68	69	70
71	72	73	74	75	76	77	78	79	80
81	82	83	84	85	86	87	88	89	90
91	92	93	94	95	96	97	98	99	100

Answers will vary.

Page 364

4 + 4 = 8

5 + 5 = 10

6 + 6 = 12

7 + 7 = 14

8 + 8 = 16

Extra: 6, 8, 10, 12, 14, 16

Pattern: Count by 2s, even numbers, doubling

Page 365

5

Child's patterns and equations will vary.

Page 366

Answers will vary.

Page 367

Answers will vary.

Page 368

Answers will vary.

Page 369

15; 8

Page 370

Alex's coins: 5¢ + 25¢ + 10¢ = 60¢

Billy's coins: 10¢ + 10¢ + 10¢ + 10¢ + 10¢ + 5¢ + 5¢ + 1¢ + 1¢ + 1¢ = 63¢

63¢ > 60¢ Billy has more money.

Page 371

1¢: 10 coins for 10¢

5¢: 4 coins for 20¢

10¢: 2 coins for 20¢

25¢: 2 coins for 50¢

Page 372

Answers will vary.

Page 373

9 centimetres, 5 centimetres, 3 1/2 centimetres, 7 1/2 centimetres

Patty, Peter, Petunia, Paul

Page 374

pencil: 5

lunchbox: 2 1/2

crayon: 5

notebook: 2 1/2

Page 375

1 gallon = 4 litres

1 litre = 4 250 ml containers

1 250 ml container = 1 cup

1 cup = 12 tablespoons

1 tablespoon = 3 teaspoons

Page 376

2 1/2 + 5 + 2 1/2 + 5 = 15 centimetres

5 + 7 1/2 + 5 + 7 1/2 = 25 centimetres

5 + 12 1/2 + 5 + 12 1/2 = 35 centimetres

Page 377

book height: 2 centimetres

book width: 3 centimetres

straw: 6 centimetres

marker: 4 centimetres

5 cubes: 4 centimetres

10 cubes: 8 centimetres

shoe: 5 centimetres

hand: 3 centimetres

Page 378

Answers will vary. The following is a likely answer. Check children's graphs to make sure that they correspond to the boxes checked.

chicken: see, hear, smell, touch

sun: see

lemonade: see, touch, taste

flowers: see, smell, touch

drums: see, hear, touch

Page 379

Answers will vary.

Page 380

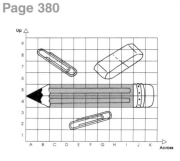

Page 381

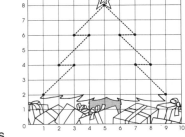

Page 382

Sunny days: 12

Cloudy days: 8

Rainy days: 5

Snowy days: 6

Page 383

Colour shapes 1, 2, 5, 6, 7, and 8.

Page 384

1/5 of the circle, 4/5 of the rectangle, 3 ants, 2 spiders, 0 bees, 5 worms

Page 385

1/8 of the circle, 6/8 of the square, 4 suns, 8 stars,

2 moons, 3 planets

Page 386

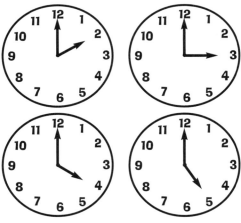

Page 387

Page 388

Page 389

Answers will vary.